CAPERNAUM
CENTURION

by

Lee Webber

Flip over for another great novel!
CALL ME SARAH

A BARBOUR BOOK

© 1991 Barbour and Company, Inc.

P.O. Box 719
Uhrichsville, OH 44683

Printed in the United States of America

ISBN 1-55748-172-5

Typesetting by Typetronix, Inc.
Cape Coral, Florida

1

Castor Fabius sat on a bench in his garden and enjoyed the warming rays of the early morning sun. "It will be a fine day," he said aloud, although there was no one to hear his deep, melodious voice. Since he had retired a year ago, the old centurion had enjoyed his privacy and the solitude that had been denied him since the day he enlisted to serve his country as a Roman soldier. There was not much private time in the army. Every movement was programmed and controlled. The sound of the trumpet put them to bed and the sound of the trumpet got them out of bed. The sound of the trumpet announced the meals, and all the men of the centurion's company ate as a family. The sound of the trumpet announced the daily exercises, which were as organized and exhausting as a true battle. In fact, they were always on a wartime footing, always ready, always at full strength. No wonder they had conquered and held the world.

And Castor had done his part. He relaxed and stretched out his strong legs in front of him, still bearing the marks of the brass greaves that had been part of his attire for most of his life. "Yes, I have done my part," he said to himself, "and now I will enjoy the fruits of my labors."

Rome was certainly not stingy with those who had served her well, and Castor was an example of that. He had been retired with honors, and with a sizable severance pay — four hundred thousand talents — and this made it possible for him to buy this fine villa, giving him the status of a Roman knight, and have enough remaining to live comfortably for the rest of his life.

So far, he had enjoyed his retirement. Only occasionally would he make the short trip to Rome, but often the things he saw disturbed him more than amused him. "I don't know about this younger generation," he would mutter to himself as a group of young people passed him, dressed in what, at least to him, was outlandish dress. "And the parties!

Did I risk my life to make this way of life possible?" But then his pride in the role he had played in upholding the best qualities of Roman rule in the world would return, and he often said to himself after doubts had assailed, "It was worth it; I have no regrets."

He stirred on the bench, turning slightly to let the sun warm another side, and thought about the meeting he was about to have. There was a large villa just to the north of his, and he had become friends with his new neighbor, a teacher and philosopher. Although Castor did not understand all his obtuse concepts, their conversation was lively, and both Castor and his neighbor Gaius had come to realize that nothing gave one an understanding of the true nature of affairs like experience in the real world, and the real world was to be found far beyond the city limits of Rome.

"I have a son," Gaius had said one day, speaking slowly to choose his words well, "I have a son who is a very intelligent boy who aspires to be an historian. Perhaps this has been his destiny since I named him Livy, in honor of our greatest Roman historian." Gaius paused for a moment or two, wondering if he should pursue the subject further. He glanced up at Castor's face to see if he could get any encouragement from his expression, and since he thought he sensed an honest openness, he decided to make his request. "My son Livy has asked me … that is to say, we have talked about this, and I think it is a splendid idea … that is if you think well of it …"

Castor saw that his neighbor was struggling to ask for some favor and having a difficult time of it, so he interrupted him with a smile, laid his large, warm hand on his shoulder, and said, "You wanted to ask me for a favor, is that right?"

"Well, yes," replied Gaius, "but I do not know how you will take it. You see, Livy would like to ask you about your experiences in Galilee, and write them down."

"Is that all?" laughed Castor. "I thought something serious was coming. That will be no problem; I will be happy to speak to the boy."

"Fine, fine," said Gaius, with a serious look on his face. "But, you see, there is a bit more than that. He would like to come to talk with you more than once — more than twice. He wants to write a book that he hopes will give the students here a view of the world beyond Rome, those places they have never heard about, how life is out there on the fringes. You must have many stories to tell that would make this history come alive."

Gaius paused, wondering if he had pushed too hard; perhaps he should have mentioned the idea in passing, and come back to it another time. But Livy had his heart set on this project. Now it was in Castor's hands. When Castor hesitated, Gaius thought that his chances were slight, but Castor paused, not because he was thinking of refusing, but because a flood of long-forgotten memories flooded his mind. How often he had told himself, "What a tale I will have to tell when this is over!" But then he turned to Gaius and said, almost as though he was thinking out loud, "I could never get all my thoughts organized."

"Leave that to Livy," said Gaius. "It is the job of the historian to analyze and organize; but first he must have the information—what happened, how it happened, why it happened. No doubt you could supply this."

"Indeed I could!" said Castor with rising enthusiasm. "I have seen more things and have been a part of more events than any two men living here in Rome. Yes, I could tell an interesting story."

"Then you agree to this?" asked Gaius with undisguised pleasure. "It will mean much to Livy, and who knows, what he writes may make a great contribution to our understanding of the events that have shaped our lives."

So it had been decided, and the young historian to be would be coming at any moment now. Castor had spoken to him a few times and thought he was a fine young man, but to the eyes of the old centurion, he was on the frail side, hardly a man to be placed on the front line, better suited to the pen than the sword. Livy was short, hardly coming up to the centurion's shoulder, with fair skin that proclaimed that his time had been spent in school and study, rather than on the exercise field. He seemed timid, too, with his "Yes, sir; no, sir" said in an almost pleading voice. But perhaps he felt out of place in the world of his elders. No doubt he would be more in his element with his pen in hand.

Livy arrived precisely at the time appointed—no doubt he always did — and seemed cautious in his approach to Castor. Too thankful, too solicitous, thought Castor, but no doubt, he will feel more at ease once we begin.

"Where shall we begin?" asked Castor in his most casual voice.

"I really don't know," replied Livy. "I was hoping that you would be able to tell me. I don't want to write a history book that is a dry accounting of what happened first, and what happened next. I am more concerned with the people — their motives, their reactions — that sort of thing. If you will just talk to me and tell me what you saw, what you heard, what you felt, I will try to take it from there."

Castor smiled to himself. *I like this lad, and I think he knows what he is doing. I think I am going to enjoy these sessions. It will do me good to gather my thoughts and stir old memories. I do have a story to tell.*

"Where shall I begin?" asked Castor, leaning back on the bench and rubbing his chin thoughtfully. He did not wait for Livy to respond, but continued. "Let me be the philosopher for a moment. All of history, it seems to me, is like a huge tapestry containing many scenes. All the threads are interwoven, and if you follow a single thread, you will find it appearing again and again, first in this scene, and then in the next. If you pull out that one thread, you will mar many scenes, but most of the time, we see only one scene at a time, and so we do not realize that they are all interrelated. One good person, like a golden thread, can brighten many scenes, and one evil person, like a black thread, can darken just as many."

Livy thought about that for a moment, and then said, "I suppose that is true, and perhaps in some way, each person's actions affect every other person. But are you thinking about someone in particular?"

"Well, yes. Take for example, Herodias, the second wife of Herod Antipas, tetrarch of Galilee. If you give me the time, I think I can show you how this evil woman destroyed and disturbed everything she touched, even reaching to Caesar himself — yes, even to Caesar."

Castor's eyes narrowed as he looked across the hills, seemingly lost in thought, remembering things of years gone by, things he had pondered often, trying to make the pieces of the puzzle fit together. Then he roused himself and said firmly, "She destroyed John the Baptist, she debased her own daughter Salome, she was the cause of a war, and she ultimately destroyed her husband. All of this, and more, from one evil, scheming woman. That is the dark side, but there is also the golden side. Yes, I have seen the golden side, too."

"Good, good," said Livy, "that's the kind of thing I am interested in, but we have to find a beginning. Tell me where you were stationed — something about the area."

"I was stationed in Capernaum in Galilee," said Castor. I went there as centurion in the fifth year of the reign of Caesar Tiberius. Capernaum —do you know where that is? No, I don't suppose you do. Roman historians did not know we existed in that far-flung region of the empire, and the Jewish historians took no note of us, either. To them, Galilee is populated by uncultured, ignorant people who do not even deserve a mention when the great affairs of the nation are discussed. But time will prove them wrong, mark my word!

"Capernaum is located on the northwest shore of the Sea of Galilee, now officially called the Sea of Tiberias. This sea is a most remarkable body of water. I do not know how our engineers were able to calculate this, but they tell us that the sea actually lies many, many leagues below the level of the Great Sea. How a sea can be below sea level is beyond my knowledge, but I will leave that to the experts. And there is more; this sea empties into the Jordan River, which runs through a rift, going lower and lower until it empties into the Salt Sea, which some say is the lowest point on earth.

"Our Sea of Galilee is a beautiful sheet of water, often reflecting the blue sky and the surrounding hills, but it is also subject to sudden violent storms that are a danger to even the most accomplished fisherman. And fishermen are there in abundance! The sea is very good to them, providing a major industry.

"More than five thousand souls claim Capernaum as home, and they do so with pride. The houses are well built, and are large by Galilean standards. Most are constructed of stone, set without mortar, plastered with clay and lime on the outside, and artistically decorated on the inside. The roofs are flat, made of reeds and sticks, plastered with mud, and when taken care of, do a better job than one might think in keeping out the weather. In the courtyard surrounding each house, the family keeps the donkeys, sheep, goats, and chickens.

"If you were to approach Capernaum, the first thing you would see is the synagogue because it is the largest, tallest building in town." Castor paused as though he was evaluating two roads he could travel to proceed. "Modesty would dictate that I make no mention of this, but accuracy demands that I must, because it is important to the story. It is one of the threads I mentioned. I built that synagogue with my own funds. I tell you this, not to improve your opinion of me, but in order to correct a longstanding misunderstanding about Rome and its treatment of occupied area. Oh, yes, Herod thought he was in charge, but he ruled only as long as he pleased Rome, and when he ceased to do so, he was gone. You have head of 'the iron heel of Rome,' but I represented Rome in Capernaum, and the people there knew I was not their enemy but their friend.

"You must understand, Livy, that the Israelites take their religion more seriously than do the Romans. The Sabbath is sacred to them, and the synagogue is the heart of their worship. Every Friday at sundown each home is adorned and the Sabbath lamp is lit. Wearing their best garments, the family gathers around the table set with the best that the family can afford. Before the festive meal, a benediction is said over the cup of wine. In the morning they come with hurried steps to the synagogue to indicate their anticipation of the time of worship, and they return home with slow steps as though they are reluctant to leave the holy place. If you could see this, you would understand how important that place is to them."

"Isn't it unusual for a Roman centurion to build a synagogue?" asked Livy cautiously. "I don't think I have ever heard of such a thing."

"Yes, I suppose it is unusual, but I had my reasons," said Castor, leaning forward intently to make sure that Livy did not miss the import of what he was about to say. "When I first came to Capernaum, I saw that I would have to have the cooperation of the elders in order to have peace and tranquility. The man I chose to help me was a man named Ezra — a good man, an honest man — and soon we became more than allies; we became friends. When he spoke of the need for a new synagogue — a need that was obvious to me as well — I decided to take action. But there is more."

Now Castor became more intense, like a lawyer trying to make a point, trying to persuade. "I was impressed by their piety, and the evident contribution their faith made to their lives. God was real to them. I could not help but compare that to my so-called faith. The God of the Hebrew is not at all like the gods of the Roman pantheon, and this set me to thinking. My training in the Roman legion entered into this. 'Law and justice,' I was told, 'without law and justice the world is a madhouse!' I could see that, and I gave my life to that, but the Roman gods seemed to know nothing about 'law and justice.' If the world is ruled by these capricious, vindictive, and often immoral gods, then we do live in a madhouse."

Livy was quick to interrupt, "After you built the synagogue, did you attend?"

"No," replied Castor. "I could not because I was a gentile. Also I could not keep the Sabbath and still be a centurion."

"What benefit did you get out of it then?" asked Livy

"I didn't do it with the thought of benefit; I did it out of the goodness of my heart, and my genuine love for the people. Some will tell you that the Jews hate the Romans and the Romans despise the Jews, but that was not true in Capernaum. And I did receive a benefit in a most unexpected way, a way I think you will find hard to believe. But I think that is enough for a start," said Castor as he stood up, indicating that the interview was over. "See what you can make out of what I have told you."

2

Castor was waiting for Livy again, but this time his feelings were entirely different. Before the first meeting, he was unsure of the project, and thoughts and memories were swirling around in his head in complete disorder. Now he found himself trying to organize his mind, and saying to himself, "I will tell this first and then I will tell that; no, it should be the other way around." He had to admit that this new experience brought a new excitement to his quiet life, and this time he eagerly awaited the coming of his young scribe.

Livy arrived carrying his wax tablets as he did when he was a student. Each tablet had a frame of wood to keep the wax from rubbing against its neighbor, and a number of these were bound together with a cord to make a book. Of course, his final work would be done on papyrus with a brass pen and ink made of soot and a glue substance. As Livy entered the gate and came down the walk that ran down the center of the formal garden, Castor could not help thinking that he looked for all the world like a scholar on his way to school. *He must be at least twenty-two*, thought Castor. *When I was his age, I had several years of service under my belt, but I guess scholars live a different kind of life.*

After cordial greetings, Castor was ready to launch into his story, but Livy stopped him by saying, "Before we get into that, I need some local color ... about the synagogue, for example. What is it like? What do they do there?"

Castor reached behind him and picked up a dry stick and bent over to make a sketch on the flagstone at his feet. He marked out a rectangle and said, "The floor was made of large limestone slabs. Many generations of feet will pass over before it begins to show any wear at all. Then there are two rows of stone columns, here and here" — he marked out the places — "nine feet apart, supporting the central part of the roof. Three doors are in front, here, here, and here, each with a carved stone lintel over it. Over this center door, is a carving of Aaron's rod and a pot of manna. I could tell you what that means, but it wouldn't help your story."

Livy made a few notes and then asked, "What is it like inside and what do they do there?" He asked this with obvious interest; he was looking for details to fill out the picture.

"You would be surprised at the inside," replied Castor. "No gods, no images, no pictures. If you walked through the center door, here, at the far end, the south end, you would see a beautiful curtain, and in front of it, the holy lamp. Behind the curtain is the holy chest with the sacred scrolls. On a platform in front of the curtain, facing the people, are chairs for the rulers of the synagogue, and to one side, the desk at which the law is read, and a seat for the person who would deliver the address. I had no part in drawing the plans; there are strict Jewish regulations about that. I only paid the bills, and this I was well able to do. Perhaps you know that as a centurion, I received five times the pay of the common Roman soldier. But now, let me get on with my story.

"One Sabbath day, a young rabbi from Nazareth came to the synagogue. He had been baptized by John the Baptist, and John had said some prophetic things about him, so they gave him the seat of the teacher. What he said, I never heard, but what I did hear were the comments of the people when it was over—'Such power! Such authority! I never heard anything like it! We must hear him again!' Well, it wasn't long before the other synagogues in the region were asking to hear him, and his fame spread.

"But there is more. One Sabbath, he healed a man who because of some kind of mental disorder shouted out in the service. He healed him right on the spot. Believe me, that got the people excited. They started to come from all over because they heard that he could heal anyone of anything. What crowds!

"As you know, Rome does not like crowds; crowds often get out of control, so I felt it necessary to monitor this to make sure that it did not get out of hand. Then I listened to what he was saying; he spoke of righteousness and justice, and a kingdom he called the Kingdom of Heaven. He talked about meekness and peacemaking, and loving your neighbor. I must tell you that even I, a hardened Roman centurion, felt a stirring deep inside that I cannot explain."

Livy looked up from his writing and said, "That was Jesus that they called the Christ, wasn't it? I have heard some evil things about him and his followers."

"But," Castor broke in, "wait until I tell you my story before you make any judgments. I can tell you things you never heard, and perhaps will never hear on the streets of Rome." Castor could see that Livy was not convinced, but that didn't matter. This was the beginning of the story, not the end.

"Let me come now to the part of the story that is unbelievable, but true. I know … I was there!" Castor was speaking slowly and quietly to let the import of what he was about to say sink in. "I had a young assistant who was like a son to me. One morning when the trumpet blew for morning assembly, he started to get out of bed, but fell back, weak and feeling faint. I ordered him to stay in bed and sent the doctor to see him. The doctor said it was some kind of fever with weakness, so he gave him some herbs and ordered him to eat nothing but goat's milk. But he did not get better; each day he seemed to lose ground. We were attached to the Roman garrison in the capital city of Galilee, called Tiberias, several miles to the south of us on the sea. The centurion there had been with me when we were rookies, and I sent word to him that we needed medical help for my assistant. Two days later, that doctor arrived, but by then he said that the situation was hopeless and the man was going to die. I knew this was true because he was too weak even to take goat's milk, and could hardly move. The doctor was very kind and very sorry, but he turned around and made his way back to Tiberias.

"I had to do something; I couldn't just stand there and watch him die. What could I do? The I remembered what that rabbi had done — how many he had healed. Were these healings real? Did the people just imagine something had happened to them? That didn't matter now; I had no choice. That was my only chance.

"I hurried over to my friend Ezra's house and told him of my problem. He was cautious; 'I'm not sure the rabbi can do anything, and I'm not sure he is willing to help a gentile,' he told me. But I said to him, 'You will never know if you don't ask him. If he can't help, or won't help, we are no worse off than we are right now.' So Ezra hurried off.

"This is what I heard later. When Ezra told the rabbi about my need, the people around joined in to urge him to intercede, and they told him that I had been good and fair to them, and here is the main point — they told him I had built the synagogue. Without hesitation, the rabbi said, "I will go and heal the man,' and started off with the crowd following. When a runner came to me with the news, I was concerned and uneasy. I knew that no good Jew could enter a gentile's house — that was too much to ask — but without his help, my assistant would surely die. I had to find a way to solve this dilemma. I knew that the rabbi had demonstrated his authority over sickness, and he was a man of power, so I knew what I had to do. I sent a runner to meet him with this message: 'I am a man of authority, as you are. I give a command and it is carried out, and I know you can do the same. I am not worthy for you to come under my roof. Give the command! That will be enough! My servant will be healed.'

"I don't know where I got the courage to say this to him, but they tell me he was impressed and said that such faith would be rewarded. I don't know what you will think about that, but I will tell you this; by the time the sun went down, my assistant was as good as new!"

Here Castor paused, waiting for some response from Livy, but none came. "That's all right," Castor said to himself again, "my story is just beginning."

3

When Livy arrived the next morning, Castor could sense that he was slightly uneasy, and during their conversation about the weather and some news of Rome, he appeared to be looking for an opening to say something. *I know what it is,* thought Castor: *He is uneasy about our last session, and is looking for a polite way to tell me. Should I help him out, or should I let him learn how to handle an interview?* He decided on the latter.

"Sir," said Livy after he had gained his courage, "that was an interesting session we had last time, but that was not quite what I was looking for. I want to write a history of that region from a Roman point of view."

"What could be more Roman than seeing things through the eyes of a Roman centurion?" asked Castor with a smile. "But I know what you mean, and I will get to that right now. Let me start with Tiberias, the capital of Galilee. I have to give you a little history so you will appreciate what happened. When Herod the Great died, Herod Antipas presumed he would be named king. He had reason to expect this, because Herod had stipulated it in his will.

"Herodias knew this and saw her chance. She was an ambitious woman, and more than anything else, she wanted to be queen of Israel. It didn't matter that she was married to Herod's brother; it didn't matter that Herod was married to the daughter of the King of Arabia. She was the kind of woman who would let nothing stand in the way of her desires. I have seen her on my visits to Tiberias, and I must say that she is indeed a beautiful woman, with a mysterious, haunting kind of beauty. There is a fascination about her that is hard to explain. She does not charm me, but I can understand how Herod could be overwhelmed by her. I think he is completely under her control. When she went home with Herod, that set in motion a chain of events that left behind a trail of misery.

"Herod the Great did not leave the kingdom to Herod Antipas. To the surprise of everyone, he divided the kingdom among three of his sons, and Herod Antipas got Galilee and Perea, not the choice part of Judea with the city of Jerusalem. Old Herod was still reaching out his envious hand from the grave. He wanted to make sure that no one after him would ever be 'King of the Jews.' Antipas fought this, but the decision stood. He could do nothing but retire to Galilee.

"In a way, I know how he felt. When I was assigned to Galilee, I was disappointed. I had plans and ambition, and I knew that I would be buried in such an isolated place. In a way, I was right; you see that I never made it above the rank of centurion. I am not complaining, mind you, because I was able to serve my nation with honor, and I escaped the intrigue and the violence that has plagued our nation, as you well know. But I know how he felt.

"I know how Herodias felt as well. She had pictured herself as queen in the beautiful city of Jerusalem, and now look at what she had! She did not like it! She would never give up her plans to be queen — nothing could make her give up that — but in the meantime, she was not content to sit in a dusty old palace and wait. They needed something better.

" 'What we need is a new capital of Galilee', said Herod one morning as they were discussing the situation. They were in their palace beyond the Jordan by the Salt Sea. Herodias's eyes brightened. 'Yes, that's it! A capital city more magnificent and more glorious than Jerusalem itself. Jerusalem has old buildings and crooked, crowded streets. We can do better than that; we should start from scratch and lay out a city with wide streets, great public buildings, and, yes, even an amphitheater. And our palace, our palace should be the finest in the world.'

"Herod was pleased with her enthusiasm, and also with the thought that he could outdo his father in reputation as a builder of great cities. His mind raced as he thought of ideas. 'And we will call it Tiberias; yes, Tiberias. The emperor will certainly agree to that, and it will put us in line to receive some favors from him in the future.'

"Herodias had already thought of that, and she said to herself, *The one favor I want is to be queen of the whole kingdom of the Jews! Our day will come.*

"And so, in the eighth year of the reign of Caesar Tiberius, the plans were drawn and the work begun. 'By the lake,' Herodias had said. 'Somewhere high above the Sea of Tiberias.' Herod concurred. A site was chosen — a place open and empty except for reeds. The plans were drawn by Greek architects who were told to spare no expense in planning a city to rival any in the world. This would be a monument to Herod's greatness, and the world would know about him long after he had passed from the scene.

Workmen and craftsmen were brought in, some from great distances, and the work proceeded. The city was laid out, measured and marked with wide streets, a palace, an amphitheater, public buildings, and houses. It looked as though Herod and his ambitious undertaking would be a big success.

"You would think, wouldn't you, Livy, that the Jews would be happy to see this project become a success, but that was not the case. They did not like Herod, and they opposed everything he did. This animosity went back a long way; they had suffered under Herod's father, and some of that hatred spilled over to the son. They never really accepted any of the Herods as true Israelites, and many proclaimed loudly that they had no right to rule in Israel.

"Then there was the matter of John the Baptist. When he appeared in the wilderness by the river Jordan, he stirred the conscience of the people. Although the religious leaders were irritated by him, the people held him in high esteem, and deemed him to be a prophet of God. When they learned that he had been beheaded when Herodias requested it, and all because of an immoral dance by Salome, they were sure that both Herod and Herodias were incarnations of evil. Now add to that the fact that the Galileans were people who had a natural dislike for sophistication and showy display, and you can understand their ire to see this city rising on the shores of their lake. Too they were wary of the influx of foreigners, especially gentiles, into their land. I am sure that many of them were praying that God Almighty would take a hand and stop what they could not prevent.

"I don't know whether you could say that God did it, but something did happen that changed the whole matter. One morning, a gang of workmen were digging a foundation for one of the buildings when the ground suddenly gave way and they fell into a pit. No one was hurt, and it would seem that this was nothing more than an inconvenience, but that was not the case. A shout of horror went up, first from one man, then from the others, until they all ran screaming from the pit, and fled without even retrieving their tools. They ran and never returned.

"Now what do you think they could have seen to cause such a reaction? I'll tell you. They had fallen into a tomb full of bones. And why would grown men be so afraid of bones that obviously had been buried for a long, long time? I did not understand this at first, so I talked to my elder friend, Ezra, and he enlightened me. It seems that the Hebrew Scriptures state very clearly that anyone who touches a grave of dead bones shall be unclean for seven days, and must go through a ceremony of cleansing or be cut off from his people. Since Tiberias was being built on a graveyard, Ezra told me, no believing Jew would choose to live there — the whole place was unclean. So much for Herod's grand scheme!

"But Herod was stubborn, and he was not about to give up his dream. The work had progressed too far for him to admit defeat, so he ordered the work to proceed as though nothing had happened. This meant that they had to bring in men who were willing to work in a long-abandoned cemetery. He paid them, and they came, and they built the city.

"Herod remembered what he had seen in Rome, how Caesar Augustus had transformed the city by replacing the brick buildings with those made of marble. Carrara marble. Nothing less would do for Herod's palace. In front was a wide walk constructed of intricately shaped limestone blocks leading to a large portico flanked by marble columns decorated with grape clusters and leaves. Through the wide doors, one would enter the ornate great hall containing elaborate wall hangings that Herod imported from Babylon. One complete wall was a mural which gave the appearance of a window to the outside. The dining room had to be something special because Herodias planned to hold large banquets several times a week. She also gave special attention to the bedroom. It was large — larger than most entire homes — with huge windows that framed the view of the lake and faced the east to catch the rays of the rising sun. The opposite wall had similar windows to give a clear view of the sunset. Since most of the cultured people of Rome had a personal library, Herod had to have one too, and master carpenters were brought in to construct the square receptacles along the walls to hold the scrolls.

"When it was finished, it was a beautiful city, but none of the Galileans would move there. Herod offered them free land, free houses, bribes, but very few were interested, so he gave the land and houses to anyone who would come, and many did — mostly gentiles, mostly Greeks — and still the great capital of Galilee was not full. But Herod did not give up; he began to order people, to force people to move there against their wills. This is when we began to feel it in Capernaum.

"You will remember, Livy, that I talked about the recurring threads in a tapestry; here is an example. We had a silversmith in Capernaum who was ordered by Herod to move his business to Tiberias. It so happened that this man, a Greek named Alex, had worked for Herod's brother, when Herodias was still his wife. Alex was a handsome young man, and their daughter Salome had a crush on him, but he would have nothing to do with her. He considered her a show-off, and she liked to remind him of his place, that he was merely hired help. She also enjoyed tempting the men with her sensuous dances. One night she tried to seduce Alex, and when he refused, she accused him of attacking her. When Herodias heard of it, she shouted that she would see to it that he would rot in prison. Alex escaped, but Herodias felt that she had been mocked, and she never forgave him for making a fool of her.

"Alex later married a woman named Sarah, and she too had a connection with Herod and Herodias. She had worked in their palace at the time that John the Baptist was coming into prominence. When Herodias heard of his fame, she disguised herself and took Sarah with her to hear him.

"Alex and Sarah had had a tenuous relationship, but it had been interrupted when Alex fled. Sarah had given up any hope of ever seeing him again; but there he was, going down into the river to be baptized by John. In time, Herodias turned her fierce anger against John the Baptist and vowed that she would see him dead. She persuaded her husband to throw him in prison. Sarah brought him his supper and talked with him in the evenings. When John was beheaded, she left the palace in revulsion, and never returned.

"As it happens in every good love story, Alex and Sarah finally got together and were married in Jericho, but when John's disciples went to follow the rabbi from Nazareth, they followed with them. By then, the rabbi was living in Capernaum with a fisherman named Peter, and that's how Alex and Sarah happened to be in Capernaum.

"Now they were in trouble. Each felt they would be in danger from the unreasonable wrath of both Herod and Herodias if they were forced to move to Tiberias. They appealed for help to the elder Ezra, and he brought them to talk to me to see if I could help. Although I had no power over Herod's orders, I did have contacts.

"I had gone to Tiberias to see my fellow centurion Justin on business, and he had introduced me to Herod's right-hand man, his major domo, we would call him. The man's name was Kooza. Without him, Herod would be lost. Herod was actually a very lazy man, and he left the work to others whenever he could. It was Kooza who ran the city. He was our hope, so I gave Alex and Sarah a letter to Kooza telling him of their circumstances and asking for his help. I thought I was doing them a favor, but it didn't turn out that way, and I'll tell you why.

"Alex and Sarah went to Tiberias, hoping to see Kooza and find some way around the order without having to see either Herod or Herodias, which they were sure would prove disastrous to them. When they arrived in Tiberias and were going to meet Kooza, they had to pass through the palace garden, where Herod and Herodias were sitting behind a vine-covered trellis sipping spiced wine. When Herodias saw the two coming down the walk, she tapped Herod on the shoulder and whispered intently, 'Herod, look at those two people. Do they look familiar to you?' Herod turned and gazed at them, trying to make connections, and then replied, 'The woman looks familiar, but I don't recognize the man.'

" 'That's like you, Herod,' said Herodias. 'You always have eyes for the women, especially one as beautiful as she is; but the man ... he looks familiar, too.'

"Herod was not paying much attention to what she was saying; he was searching his memory to connect a name with the face of the woman. Suddenly he said, 'Sarah! That's who she is. That's Sarah who worked for us, and then just disappeared.'

" 'You're right!' said Herodias, 'Now I remember; it's all coming back to me now. But the man ... I know him too.' She raised her hand as a sudden inspiration came to her. 'I've got it! He's the one that Salome accused of attacking her, remember? He escaped through a small window and ran. Well, well; now it appears that the two fugitives have gotten together. I wonder what they are doing here.'

" 'What shall we do with them?' asked Herod. 'Maybe we ought to teach them a lesson.'

" 'Maybe we ought to do more than that,' replied Herodias."

Livy broke into the story and asked, as a good historian should, "How could you know what they said to each other? Are you just assuming that this happened?"

"No, I'm not just assuming," replied Castor. "Kooza was coming to ask Herod about another matter, and he heard it all. They were so intent on what they were seeing that they never knew he was there. When he made his presence known by a discrete cough, Herod confronted him directly with the question, 'What are those two people doing here?' Since Kooza had never met them, he replied honestly, 'I don't know, but perhaps the man is the silversmith from Capernaum who is coming to see me.'

" 'Then we will see them together,' said Herod. 'Have them brought to the audience room.'

"When Alex and Sarah were told that they were to have an audience with Herod and Herodias, they knew they were in trouble. Sarah is a woman of great faith in God, and in times of need, she always resorted to prayer. Before going in with the servant, she led Alex behind a column and quickly prayed, 'O Lord God, our times are in Your hands, and You lead the steps of those who put their trust in You. Come to our aid, we pray, and make the path smooth before us. Amen.' Then, with confidence, they went in for the audience.

"Herodias, especially, enjoyed having people at a disadvantage, and liked to see people grovel before her, and she intended to make the most of this situation. She went to her room, put on her finest robe, selected a tiara that looked like a crown, and placed some of her largest rings on her fingers. She intended to overwhelm Sarah with her regal appearance.

"When Alex and Sarah entered the audience room, Herod looked at them sternly and said in his most menacing voice, 'So here we have two fugitives from justice! Tell me, what should the punishment be?'

"Alex bowed his head slightly in deference to Herod's position, and then said quietly, 'My Lord, we are both fugitives, it is true, but not from justice.'

" 'All criminals contend that they are innocent,' sneered Herod, 'and all of them think they have good reasons for fleeing. I didn't expect you to be any different.' Then he noticed the letter in Alex's hand, the letter that I had given him. Since he had no appointment with Alex, Herod knew that the letter was not for him, but he said just the same, 'Do you have a letter of defense for me? Let me see it.'

"Alex said quietly, 'The letter is addressed to someone else.' He knew what I had written, and he knew how it would sound to Herod. Herod knew he had him in a trap, and he intended to spring it.

" 'Whose name is on the letter?' asked Herod in a mocking voice.

" 'It is addressed to Kooza', replied Alex in a steady but frightened voice.

" 'Then give it to him,' said Herod.

"Alex handed the letter to Kooza and hoped for the best, but the best did not come. Herod commanded Kooza, 'Now give the letter to me.'

"Kooza was about to protest about private communications, but thought better of it, and with a bow of his head, he handed the letter to Herod.

"Herod scanned the letter, and then began reading portions out loud. ' "… They are completely innocent." Ha! If they were innocent, they would have nothing to fear, and they would not have gone to a centurion for help.' Then he read in a loud voice, ' "... and Sarah had to escape the evil woman Herodias, and could no longer stay in the palace where they had beheaded the prophet of God, John the Baptist." '

"Herodias's eyes blazed, and she spit out her words as though they were flames of fire burning in her mouth. 'So we are so evil that you cannot stand to be under the same roof with us! You are so holy and pure! And we are the minions of Satan himself! Who could blame you for fleeing!'

"During this time, Sarah stood with her head bowed, saying nothing. This annoyed Herodias, so she screamed at her, 'How would you like to taste some of that evil ... raining down on your pure, innocent head ... good swallowed up by evil? How would you like that?' She was trembling with rage, speaking almost incoherently.

"Sarah replied in a voice so low that it could hardly be heard, 'The Lord is my helper; I will not fear what man can do to me.'

"Herod broke in to divert the attention from Herodias, and said, 'So you have the Lord to help you, and you do not need the help of Herod. Then why come here looking for help? Why didn't you just tell the Lord that you didn't want to move to Tiberias? I'll tell you why you didn't! You needed Herod's help, and you were afraid to ask for it. Well, I will show you that I can do what the Lord couldn't do for you. I rescind my order. I forbid you to move to Tiberias. I never want to see you here again, and if I do, you will suffer for it! Now, get out of my sight!' "

Castor paused as though the drama of the story had exhausted him. Livy had been listening so intently that he had written nothing. Then he asked, "Why would Herod just let them go? That doesn't seem to be in character for him."

"I can answer that," said Castor. "Herod had a guilty conscience because of what he had done to John, what Herodias had forced him to do to John. He was afraid that Herodias would force him to do something just as terrible to Alex and Sarah, and his conscience could bear no more. But Herodias was furious at him for his actions, calling him a weakling and a coward, and she wouldn't speak to him for weeks.

"Alex and Sarah went home praising God for their deliverance, which, you must admit, was remarkable. They never expected to deal with Herod again, but the tangled threads of the tapestry would make it otherwise, and Sarah would have been lost without the help of Herod."

4

"Are you pleased with your history so far?" called Castor as Livy came up the walk for the next session.

"Too early to tell," replied Livy. "I will need much more material before I can develop a plan, but I will tell you this; I think we are on to something. I spent yesterday in the library hunting for material with very meager results."

Castor knew that library. Caesar Augustus had built it on Palatine Hill, and it was a magnificent building. It had separate rooms for Latin and Greek texts, and a large reading room which was usually filled with scholars, students, and common citizens eager to glean the wisdom of the world. Castor knew that a man like Livy would consider that place a second home.

"You were unsuccessful, then?" asked Castor.

"Surprisingly so," responded Livy. "I was looking for background material on Galilee, but according to my fellow historians, it doesn't exist and whatever happens there is of no concern to those who live in Rome. I could not even find a mention of this Jesus in Galilee, although I could find plenty of references to the Christians in Rome, even in Caesar's household."

Castor smiled and said, "I could tell you more about the Christians in Caesar's household than you will find in the books, but that is not the place to start. It starts in Galilee, and then to Jerusalem, and from there, everywhere. But today I want to tell you about another meeting of Herod and Sarah, and soon we will get on to weightier matters.

"As I told you, Alex was a silversmith and had a good business. Although Capernaum sounds like the end of the world to you, it is on the main trade route from Damascus to Alexandria, Egypt. Alex also had been established in Jericho and had contacts in Jerusalem, so he could sell all he produced." Livy had a puzzled look on his face. "What would he produce?" he asked. "Our silversmiths make idols and statues, and

I understand that they are forbidden in Israel."

"That is true," said Castor, "but there is a big market for souvenirs from the city of Jerusalem, the Temple, the walls. There are also religious symbols that are important to them; a bunch of grapes borne on a staff by two men, a Passover lamb, a sheaf of grain — things like that. And then, of course, there is the whole market of jewelry for the wealthy. There is plenty of work for a good artist, and Alex was one of the best, and he had good men working for him. He had an excellent reputation.

"Several times a year, Alex would make a business trip to sell new merchandise in Jerusalem and Jericho and to settle accounts. This time they were taking four donkeys, and Sarah decided that she would go along and visit her father who was living in Jerusalem. They passed by my camp on the way out of town, and we talked for a while. I knew the two men who were going with them, so we had a friendly conversation. Little did I realize then that that trip would almost be the end of both of them.

"The trip to Jerusalem was uneventful, and the business successful. Sarah had a good visit with her father, but she was concerned that he was beginning to show his age. The nagging maladies that always seem to accompany the passing years were beginning to take their toll on him. They made plans for the next time they would be in Jerusalem for a feast and said their good-byes, and went on their way.

"Jerusalem, like Rome, is built on hills, but Jericho is on the Jordan River near the place where it empties into the Salt Sea, far below sea level. This means that the road is downhill for its course of twenty miles. Much of it is through wild, often deserted territory, and it is a well-known haunt for robbers. For this reason, travelers usually travel in groups for safety. Alex and Sarah and the two men with them joined some merchants from Damascus and two men from Babylon. When they got close to Jericho, Alex decided to send his two men ahead to prepare for their arrival in town. Alex and Sarah were at the rear of the small procession, talking together and enjoying the fine day, and they did not notice that at the turn of the road, the rest of the party was out of sight. They descended into a hollow where the road turned sharply to the right, and scrubby trees cast their shadow on the road. From one of these trees, they heard a sharp, short whistle, and they decided that they had better catch up with the rest of the group, but they were too late. Seemingly out of thin air, five rough-looking men surrounded them.

Alex immediately called out for help, but the turn in the road and the trees swallowed up his cry. His traveling companions went on, not even aware that they were missing. They were alone and were no match for these violent men, armed with staffs and clubs.

"The men did not attack at once — they played a little cat and mouse moving aside as if to let them pass, then rushing to close the gap, doing it so suddenly that it frightened the donkeys Alex and Sarah were riding. Alex wondered if they would be better off on foot because they were in danger from the frightened animals, as well as the men threatening them, but he decided against that; they would surely be lost on foot. What could they do? Alex thought he should try to reason with the attackers. The leader of the group was obvious because he gave the orders and the others followed without hesitation, but he did not look like a man to be reasoned with. He was large and unkempt with dirty, rumpled clothes. His face was scarred, revealing a record of many fights, some lost and some won. One scar ran up the left of his face and across his eye, bisecting his bushy eyebrow, and his eye appeared to have lost its usefulness. On his right hand, part of the middle finger was missing, and his bare arms were a collection of welts and scars. No, he did not look like a man who would be open to reason.

"But perhaps he could be bribed. In his leather belt around his waist, Alex carried a considerable amount of money from his transaction in Jerusalem. How much would it take to buy their freedom? Foolish thought! The robbers were going to take everything without making any bargains. And what about Sarah? This is what bothered Alex most. He is determined that he would defend her to the death; but what good would that do? If she survived, his death would be a crushing burden for her to bear, and she might rather choose not to survive knowing that he gave his life for hers. These thoughts ran through his mind in a moment, and he knew that while he was hopelessly searching for an answer to their predicament, Sarah was praying.

" 'Come on, Kish, let's take them and get out of the road'—it was one of the other men speaking — 'we don't want to be out here when the next bunch of travelers comes along.'

"I was just beginning to enjoy myself,' laughed Kish, 'I especially enjoy teasing a beautiful woman like this. Come with me, woman, and I will let your man go. You don't need him; what good is he to you now? He can't even protect you.' Then Kish laughed a crude, obscene laugh, and pointing to Alex, said in a taunting voice, 'What are you going to do to protect your woman? Let her go and save your own life.'

"Alex answered him with one resolute word: 'Never!'

"Kish said, 'You see how reasonable and kind I am; I offer to let you go, and I offer to protect the woman with all my strength; and you refuse my kindness. What more can I do?' With one swift leap he approached Sarah from behind and grabbing her by the hair, pulled her off the donkey, wrapping his arms around her, pinning Sarah's arms to her side so she struggled like a helpless, trapped bird. Just as quickly, Alex leaped off his donkey and advanced on Kish, intending to free his wife or die in the attempt. If Kish continued to hold Sarah, Alex figured he would have an advantage, and if he freed her to fight, she would have a chance to flee. All of this was wishful thinking; he had taken only a few steps when one of the other men swung his staff in an accurate, practiced arc and caught Alex on the side of his head. The blow was so vicious that Alex never staggered, but fell to the ground in a heap. Sarah, seeing this, screamed and fainted.

"It was a good thing for her that she fainted. What happened next, she would not want to see. Kish grabbed Alex by the hair and dragged him off the road and pulled off his robe, which by now was bloody from the wound the staff inflicted. With a shout of triumph, he undid the money belt and held it high over his head like a trophy won in battle. 'Take the rest of his clothes too,' said Kish. Then he looked at Alex lying in his own blood and said in anger, 'He was a handsome man, and there is nothing that I hate more than a handsome man!' His eyes filled with rage, and his face was contorted with hatred, and he began to beat the helpless body of Alex as though he was venting all the anger he had stored up against a world that had spurned him because he was so ugly. This was too much for one of the robbers, who stepped in and held Kish's arm. 'The man is dead,' he said. 'Let the dead be in peace.'

" 'You are too soft for this business,' said Kish in a voice dripping with scorn. 'You ought to get a job tending sheep.' Then in an act of final anger, he deliberately kicked Alex in the face and said, 'See what one well-aimed kick can do to a handsome face.' Then he turned his attention to Sarah who was beginning to stir. When she saw what they had done to Alex, she covered her face and wept.

"Kish had no sympathy for her tears; he was annoyed by them, so he commanded in a threatening voice, 'Shut up, woman, or I will give you something to cry about.' Then he roughly pulled her to her feet and bound her arms tightly behind her. He also tied her feet, but more loosely so she was able to hobble, but she could not run. Then he ordered the other men, 'Pick up everything and let's get out of here!' In single file, they slipped through a narrow opening in the underbrush and made their way around a small hill to their campsite.

"Sarah found walking on the uneven ground almost impossible, but she stumbled along, pushed from behind, pulled from in front. The short walk to the camp left her exhausted and bruised, and soon as she was allowed, she slumped to the ground in a dejected heap.

"In front of the small clearing was a cave, which served as a home for the robbers, and it was there that they deposited their loot. A pain pierced Sarah as she saw Alex's money belt, but when one of the men tried Alex's bloody robe on for size, she began to weep softly again. Her situation appeared to be absolutely hopeless, but the words to a prayer she had prayed as a child came to mind, 'O God, help of the helpless, come to my aid, I pray, and deliver me.'

"In time, Sarah became aware of her surroundings and she said to herself, 'I must be strong and alert; it may be that the Lord will make a way for me to escape even though there seems to be no way.' Any optimism she had, however, quickly evaporated as she noticed that one of the men, a man Kish had called Hab and seemed to be second in command, was watching her and looking at her with lecherous eyes. He appeared to be watching for a time when the others were occupied with their duties to make his move. He edged closer and closer to her, and Sarah thought of crying out, but before she did so, the man was on her, pushing her backward on the ground, with his mouth on hers in a violent kiss. Tied as she was, Sarah's struggles were fruitless, and she wept more out of frustration than anger. Then, suddenly, the weight was off her, and when she opened her eyes, she saw that Kish had lifted Hab bodily, and with one swing of his huge arm, smashed Hab in the face as he yelled, 'The woman belongs to me; you keep your filthy hands off of her.'

"By now, the others had gathered around, and when Hab felt the blood running down his face, his anger rose within — anger mixed with shame because Kish had humiliated him.

" 'We agreed to share and share alike,' shouted Hab. 'You didn't capture her by yourself, you know. She belongs to all of us.'

"Sarah's blood ran cold when she heard this. If this came to a vote, the others would gang up against Kish, and she would become common property. Kish recognized that this was more than a fight over Sarah; this was a challenge to his authority, and he could not allow that, so he decided to make a frontal attack. 'I will tell you what you can do and what you can't do, and I will decide what we share and what we don't share. Do you understand that?'

" 'So you want a show-down, do you?' shouted Hab. 'You think you can order everyone around, and we have nothing to say about it. Well, we're not going to take it anymore.' Hab turned to the others, hoping to gain their support for the declaration he had made. But that was a mistake; he was looking the other way when Kish's fist smashed into the side of his head, knocking him over backwards. While Hab was struggling to get up on his knees, Kish ran and got his club and approached him menacingly.

" 'So you want to fight it out, do you?' he said with obvious relish. 'We will decide this here and now.' Somebody threw Hab a staff, and the two combatants circled around looking for an opening. Hab's longer staff gave him the advantage of reach, but Kish's heavy club would deal a more lethal blow. Kish rushed and Hab stood his ground and jabbed at him with the staff, catching him in the stomach, and when Kish doubled over in pain, Hab brought the staff down across his back with a heavy blow. Kish retreated out of reach of the staff, but then charged again, with the same results.

"Now Kish was like a wild man, seemingly oblivious to the pain, and he rushed again. This time, when Hab jabbed him, he caught the staff and jerked it out of his hands, and at the same time he swung his club and aimed at Hab's head intending to finish him with one blow. As the club was falling, Hab dodged to one side, but the club caught him on the shoulder and he fell to his knees with his right arm hanging useless at his side. Now Hab was helpless, and Kish took his time and moved in for the kill. Hab bowed his head expecting this to be the end, but the blow did not fall.

"One of the men, seeing what was about to happen, rushed in and grabbed Kish's arm shouting, 'Don't do it, Kish. You've killed one man already today. That's enough.' Kish let his club fall to the ground and turned to walk away. After a few steps, he sat down heavily and called for the wine bottle. Evidently some of the jabs by Hab's pole had injured him more than he had realized in the heat of battle. As for Hab, his injured arm hung limply at his side, and he asked one of the men to get a sash to tie the arm to his body.

"When it came time to eat, Kish untied Sarah's arms, but seeing the defiance in her eyes, decided he would have to take precautions to keep

her from escaping. He was right, she carefully watched every movement, and after seeing the result of the fight, she felt hopeful that an
opportunity would develop. But she had not reckoned on the suspicious
mind of Kish. He did not leave her sitting on the ground for a moment,
although her feet were hobbled. He dragged her to a tree, pushed her to
a sitting position, and tied her to the trunk with a stout rope, making sure
that the knots were behind the tree. She could never escape from that.
Then he brought her a chunk of bread and a piece of cheese, but Sarah
refused to take it from his hand. This infuriated Kish, so he threw the
food in her lap and said to her, 'You had better eat to keep up your
strength; you will need it tonight.' Then he laughed a long raucous laugh
and turned away.

"Sarah was well aware of her situation, and decided to attack her
problem in the only way left to her — prayer. She prayed with
confidence born of years of trust in God; she prayed in confidence, not
in fear. Her heart was wounded because of what had happened to Alex,
and her situation promised only terror. But she knew that God was still
in His heaven, and she knew that He would hear her prayer and would
not abandon her in her time of greatest need. So she prayed: 'Oh Lord,
when Your servant Daniel was cast into the den of lions, You did not
allow them to hurt him, and in the morning he was safe and praising You.
I beseech You, O Lord, do the same for me! I do not know how this can
be done, but I rest my life and my body in Your tender care and I trust
you for a sunrise of blessing tomorrow. Amen.'

"Sarah was hungry, and she looked at the bread and cheese in her lap,
and was about to eat when she remembered John the Baptist and what
he had done. John had been invited to preach at a banquet in Herod's
palace, and although his friends urged him not to go, he felt that he had
a message from God to deliver there, so he went. The banquet was a
lavish and wasteful display of wealth and frivolity, and John was
completely out of place. He would not recline at the banquet tables
which were loaded with delicacies, but sat on the floor in the corner
wearing his camelhair coat while surrounded by people wearing rich,
imported clothes. Sarah herself had brought his food, but he refused to
eat; he would not take part, and he would not eat their food. 'Neither will
I,' said Sarah defiantly, and pushed the food out of her lap.

" 'Oh oh!' laughed Kish, 'we have a spirited one here. She is like a
colt that needs to be broken, and she will be before I am through with
her.'

"Sarah said nothing; she had said all she needed to say in her prayer to God.

"While they were eating, one of the men said to Kish, 'You shouldn't have taken the woman; she will make trouble for us. You can't keep her tied to a tree forever, and you can't let her go. What can you do with her?'

" 'Don't worry about that. When I get through with her, she will be so ashamed that she will never tell anybody about what happened here; she will just run away and hide,' said Kish. 'But I don't intend to let her go for a long time.'

" 'She will be trouble for us, mark my word,' continued the man. 'Look what this has done already — you and Hab.'

" 'Hab!' shouted Kish. 'Where is Hab?' Hab was gone, and no one remembered seeing him go, but this did not worry Kish. 'The coward has probably crawled off someplace to nurse his wounds. Don't worry about him. He knows better than to come around here.'

"He did know better than to return — he did not intend to return. He had walked to the road, trying to formulate his plan. First of all, he had to do something about his arm, but most of all...yes, most of all, he had to find some way to get even with Kish. Kish would pay for this, he would pay dearly, but what Hab would do, or could do, he did not know. But one thing he did know...his revenge would be swift and sweet.

"Since Jericho was the nearest town, he started in that direction, although he did not know what he would do when he got there. He would wait for something to develop. Something did — a lot sooner than he had expected, and much more promising than anything he had in mind.

"Herod was on his way to Jerusalem. He went often, and for several reasons, the first being that he found life in Tiberias quite boring when compared with the city life of Jerusalem. For another, as long as he was in Tiberias, someone was always bothering him with business, someone was always begging for a favor or worse, expecting him to do the impossible. When he was away, Kooza handled it all, and that was fine with Herod. Finally, but not least, he did not want the people of Jerusalem to forget him; one never knew what turns history might take, and it is was wise to be prepared. So quite often he would journey to his palace, the old Maccabean palace in Jerusalem, accompanied, of course, by a large, impressive retinue and display of near-regal glory.

"Herod took fifty of his own soldiers with him under the command of a man named Abner, and he had wanted my centurion friend Justin to accompany him with as many Romans, but it was not the business of

Rome to cater to his vanity. Rome was responsible only for keeping the peace, so Justin came along with only sixteen of his men. The troop, however, was augmented by servants and helpers, and taken together, they made quite a procession. They certainly made a stir when they passed through a town, and they were careful to make sure that the people knew that this was the mighty Herod on his way to Jerusalem.

"This was the procession Hab saw coming his way, and he made his plans instantly. When they were within earshot, he began to call out loudly, 'Help! Oh, help! I have been set upon by robbers who have wounded me and robbed me. Help! Help!'

"One of the heralds who led the procession was filled with pity at his sad plight, and took him immediately to Abner. Hab told his elaborate story with great emotion, and concluded by saying, 'And I escaped, and I know the way to their camp. Follow me, and you will be able to capture them easily.'

"Abner listened with a mixture of unbelief and disinterest; it was not his business to rid Judea of its robbers. Besides, this would disrupt their timetable, and perhaps would produce nothing. When Hab saw that he had no interest in this, he began to plead and beg, but to no avail. Hab was on his knees wailing when Herod came up to see why the procession had halted. Hab bowed his head to the ground, and although he knew well that Herod was no king, he said in a most lamentable voice, 'Oh King, O great King! have mercy on me and avenge me. I am a humble merchant, and the robbers have wounded me and taken my money belt with all my living. I beg you, avenge me.' Herod hesitated; this was not his territory, and he did not want to get involved. He started to turn away, and in desperation, Hab called out, 'And they have captured a beautiful woman and have her tied to a tree, and they intend to do awful things to her.'

"Herod turned on his heel; this was a different matter. He called Justin and said to him, 'It is Rome's business to keep the roads safe for travelers. Take over this matter and see what you can do.'

"Hab began to thank Herod profusely, even kissing the hem of his robe, but this simply annoyed Herod, and he turned and walked away. Justin said to Hab curtly, 'Get up! we have work to do, but if you are leading us into a trap, it will go hard on you.' He then called his men, and they started down the road at such a pace that Hab had difficulty keeping up with them.

"Hab directed them to the opening in the underbrush and led them along a path that could be discerned only by a practiced eye. When they came to the edge of the hill that shielded the camp, Hab put his finger to his lips to signify silence, and pointed around the hill to the left, and then moved behind to a place of safety. He wanted to be near enough to see Kish get what was coming to him, but far enough away to avoid danger.

"When Justin and his men burst into the clearing, the robbers were taken completely by surprise. Kish was seated on the ground near Sarah, and started to make a move for his club, which was out of reach. Justin took a few quick steps forward, his Roman sword held in the attack position, and shouted one word of command, 'Stop!' Kish then thought he could use Sarah as a shield to make his escape, but since she was tied to the tree, this was not possible. Even as he was considering these alternatives, his companions had already been bound by the other soldiers, so Kish, realizing that his position was untenable, stood and meekly turned his back, allowing his hands to be bound behind him.

"When Justin turned his attention to Sarah, she said to him, 'I am a friend of Castor, the centurion of Capernaum.'

" 'You are?' replied Justin in surprise, 'Any friend of Castor's is a friend of mine; I will see to it that you are protected and that the wrong that has been done to you will be righted.'

" 'Thank you for your protection,' said Sarah sadly, 'but I fear that all your kindness will not serve to make up for my loss.'

"Then through her tears, she related what had happened to her and Alex.

"Justin said, 'We will take these things one at a time. First, let's collect your possessions — the money belt, the clothes — and then let us see what we can learn about Alex.'

"Sarah easily located her possessions, and Justin gave orders concerning the rest of the loot in the cave. The prisoners were tied in a string by a rope around their necks and marched down to the road. In Jerusalem they would receive Roman justice, which was very harsh, and it was entirely possible that Kish as their leader would be crucified. Hab was not to be seen; in the confusion, he had walked away.

"When Justin and Sarah reached the road, Sarah identified the place where she had seen Alex lying in his own blood. The blood stains were there, but Alex was not. When Sarah was about to weep in despair, Justin said to her, 'Don't weep too soon; you can't be sure that he is dead. Save your tears until you learn that they are really needed.'

"Herod and the whole procession had stopped a short distance down the road to wait the outcome of the unexpected adventure. When the prisoners were marched by, he smiled contentedly. 'This will be a feather in my cap,' he said. 'Anyone who makes the road safe for travelers is a friend of the people.' When he saw Sarah, his reaction was first surprise, and then delight. 'You never wanted to see me again, did you? You think that I am nothing but a worker of evil! What do you say now? Are you going to thank me?'

"Sarah replied, 'I am certainly thankful that I have been delivered out of my deep distress, and I am certainly thankful that you came along when you did. I thank you for any part you have played in my rescue; but I must tell you that before you came, I committed my case to God and trusted Him for deliverance. Now I see that God can use the most unlikely people to accomplish His purposes.'

"Somehow, Herod knew that she would say something like that, so rather than taking offense at her faint thanks, he said, 'Well, I am glad to hear that God can use even a person like me; this gives me encouragement.' He did not say this in sincerity, but to mock her. Then, turning to Justin he asked, 'What are you going to do with her now?'

"Justin replied, 'I will send two of my men to escort her to Jericho where she has friends. Her husband was badly beaten by the robbers and left for dead by the side of the road, but he has disappeared, and she will have to find him.'

"Sarah thought she saw a fleeting flicker of pity cross Herod's face as he turned away and said, 'Good, but it is time that we resumed our journey. Ahab! Let's go.'

"Sarah and her escorts started on their short journey to Jericho, but they had hardly gone a furlong before Sarah saw four anxious people approaching her, people she knew, people she was happy to see. Two of them, of course, were the men who had accompanied them from Capernaum, and the other two were friends with whom they had planned to stay while in Jericho. They were more than just friends. The man, James, was the one who had given Alex a job when he fled from the wrath of Herodias, and he was the one who had taken him to hear John the Baptist and started him on his spiritual journey. The woman, Ruth, had been like a second mother to Sarah when she fled from the palace after the death of John the Baptist, and she had given Sarah a home until her marriage to Alex. Both Ruth and James had been followers of John, and at John's urging had followed Jesus of Nazareth, and it was at their suggestion that Alex and Sarah had moved to Capernaum to be close to the ministry of Jesus, which was centered there.

"They were surprised to see Sarah without Alex and alarmed to see her with two Roman soldiers. 'Where is Alex? What happened?' all four asked in unison.

"In bits and pieces, Sarah sketched the story, and then, after thanking the soldiers sincerely, she released them to return to the procession. During the rest of the journey, Sarah told her story completely, prompted by questions, punctuated by exclamations of surprise. By the time they had reached home, Sarah had collected her thoughts, and the companionship and love that now surrounded her made it possible for her to evaluate her position more accurately. The sun was setting as Ruth put some food on the table, and although Ruth thought that the sadness that surrounded Sarah would make it impossible for her to eat, Sarah felt that she wanted to be prepared for the challenges she would have to face on the morrow. So after giving thanks, she ate more heartily than the rest — she had had no food all day.

"After the meal, Sarah sat for long stretches without speaking, and James and Ruth thought it best not to interrupt her thoughts. They thought she was trying to come to terms with her loss, but, in fact, she was analyzing her situation from every angle. When she finally spoke, she said with confidence, 'Alex is not dead. If he were dead, we would have found him lying beside the road. Nobody would steal a dead body. And Alex did not walk away — they had taken all his clothes. Can you picture Alex walking around like that? No! And if he could walk, where would he go?'

" 'Why of course,' replied Ruth, 'he would come here to Jericho.'

"Oh, no; he would have come looking for me, and he would have looked until he found me,' said Sarah with a confident smile. 'So what happened to him? He must have been alive, and somebody must have found him and decided to help him. And where did they go? If they had come here to Jericho, we would know about it. No, they must have gone the other way. I'll tell you where Alex is — he is in the first inn on the way to Jerusalem, and somebody is caring for him. How do I know that? If the person who found him had no intention of helping him, he would have simply passed him by. That's where he is, I am sure of it!'

" 'You may be right,' said James after giving Sarah's theory careful thought. 'I pray to God you are right! So what do we do now? It's too late to start looking for him tonight.'

" 'We will have to wait until morning' said Sarah, 'and leave him in the hands of God, and we hope, the hands of some loving stranger.'

"Sarah was so tired from the day's events that she went to bed at once, but not before her evening prayers which she concluded with the Scripture, 'I will both lay me down in peace and sleep, for You Lord make me to dwell in safety.'

"In the morning at first light, they were up, and after breakfast, they started out. Sarah sent the two men companions to look for the donkeys that had run off because, Sarah said, 'We will need *both* of them for our trip home. Find them and bring them back to Jericho and wait for us. Also, in faith, they led a donkey in addition to the ones they rode. Sarah was sure they would be returning with Alex.

"In spite of Sarah's optimism, they were all well aware of the unpleasant possibilities they could face that morning. Ruth and James did not bring this up; they knew Sarah had calculated this as well, and they figured that she would face any tragedy with courage, but only when forced to do so. Also, Sarah was so sure that she had analyzed the situation correctly that they did not want to plant needless doubts in her mind. They would know more after they had visited the first inn on the road.

"When the inn came into view, Sarah's heart began to beat with excitement; the key to all her future happiness could be hidden behind its walls. They entered quickly but the innkeeper was nowhere to be found. Most of the travelers had already left, so Sarah approached one of the servants who was busy cleaning up in a far corner. 'I must see the innkeeper at once,' said Sarah excitedly.

"The servant replied curtly, 'He's busy; you will just have to wait.'

" 'I can't wait,' said Sarah. 'This is important. Where is he?'

" 'He's busy I told you!' said the servant, losing patience. 'He's taking care of an injured man.'

" 'That man is my husband!' shouted Sarah with urgency and joy. 'Take me to him at once.'

"The servant dropped his broom and took Sarah upstairs to a room next to the innkeeper's abode. Sarah did not wait to knock but pushed the door open and rushed in. She saw someone lying on the bed, and the innkeeper carefully tending him with a basin of water and cold cloths. Sarah could not tell if it was Alex — the face was so swollen, it could have been anyone, and the profusion of bandages made positive identification well nigh impossible.

" 'Alex?' asked Sarah timidly.

"The voice she heard in reply was more beautiful to her than the music of angels, the voice she knew so well, and the voice said one word, 'Sarah!'

"Sarah ran forward to embrace him, but Alex held up a hand to stop her. 'Wait!' he said quickly, 'I hurt all over, but I would appreciate a gentle kiss on my cheek.'

"Sarah bent over and kissed him lightly as a flood of tears began to flow, tears of relief, of thanksgiving, tears of sorrow at his painful condition. Her tears fell like rain until Alex finally said, 'Sarah, it would be a shame for me to survive the beating only to perish in a sea of salty tears.'

"This was so unexpected that Sarah began to laugh heartily. The tension was broken; the emotions that were wound tight as a twisted rope were released. Then turning to the innkeeper, Sarah asked, 'How did he get here?'

" 'A man found him lying beside the road and brought him here. He took care of him last night, but then he had to leave, he gave me money to take care of him for two days. I think he will be able to travel tomorrow. He has no broken bones, and the swelling is beginning to go down. Although he looks bad now, in a short time he will be as good as new.'

" 'How can I ever thank that man?' asked Sarah. 'He gave me back my most precious possession. I can never properly repay him. Who is he? Where can I find him?'

" 'I don't know much about him, and I don't know where you can find him,' said the innkeeper. 'He comes by here occasionally, but not on a regular basis. All I know about him is that his name is Seema, and he is a Samaritan.' "

5

"I'm beginning to get a feel for this history," said Livy. "I have started writing and some things are becoming clear. It seems to me that Caesar was willing to let the Jews do pretty much as they wished as long as they did not challenge Rome. You seemed to get along well with the people; obviously, you knew how to do your job without antagonizing the Galileans."

"Yes, that's true," said Castor. "You must remember, however, that Jewish life revolved around their religion, and all the real conflicts came when Rome was insensitive to this. This struggle continually threatened to destroy the nation entirely, and I predict that one day it will, but sometimes the prohibitions of their religion were a real disadvantage to them. Let me tell you about one event in which I was involved. In order to tell the story correctly, I will have to back up a bit, and again, you will see the interwoven threads of history.

"One day Herod and his right-hand man Kooza were in Herod's palace going over some matters of business. I think I told you that Herod was really very lazy and didn't want to do much of the work, but at the same time, he did not want to give up any of his power or control, so he would have these sessions with Kooza to make sure Kooza knew who was boss. On this morning while they were talking business, the door opened and Kooza's wife, Joanna, walked in, not walking in a normal way, but walking as though she was in a trance, and I suppose she was. To understand this, I will have to explain to you what had happened to her.

"Joanna should never have gotten herself into this situation. She had been feeling depressed, possibly because she had no children, and for a Jewish woman, this brings a feeling of failure. She had a life of relative luxury and ease, but this added to her feeling of uselessness. Her husband was at the beck and call of Herod, and this left him little time for himself, and less for his wife. She was bored, depressed, discouraged, longing for something that would brighten her jaded life.

"One afternoon she went walking in the large Greek section of Tiberias. There, in this Jewish capital city, she found a shrine to the Greek god Apollo hidden away in a garden, and a woman, a priestess, who had what they call 'a spirit of divination,' or more specifically, 'a spirit of Python.' It was called that because that was the name given to the Delphic oracle. According to Greek mythology, a huge python terrorized the area around Delphi, attacking men and animals, and the god Apollo slew it with his arrows — when he was only five days old! In Delphi, located on the southern slope of Mount Parnassus, is the oldest, most influential sanctuary in all of Greece. The priestess who gives the prophecies there is called Pythia. Some say that the prophecies can mean whatever you make them to mean, but the oracle is consulted about all important matters of government and economics, and so it had influenced all of Greek life and history.

"At first Joanna watched with only casual interest as this woman told fortunes for the people who came to her. This was new to Joanna. Interesting, forbidden by Jewish law, she knew, but she did not leave. When the priestess noticed her standing there, realizing that she was wealthy and Jewish — her garments told her that — and perhaps realizing that she was a bored woman, she fixed her piercing eyes on her as though she could see into the depths of her soul. Then she began to prophesy about her in an agitated, hysterical voice, and said some things that made Joanna feel that she could see all the hidden secrets of her soul. From that moment on, the priestess exercised a strange control over her, and she returned again and again.

"As the days passed, Joanna's confusion and depression increased to the point that she begged the priestess for help, willing to do anything she would command. The priestess told her that she had been especially chosen by Apollo, and the spirit of Python wanted to make her great and ecstatically happy. All she had to do to obtain this was to unlock the door of her spirit and invite him in. Whether Joanna did this of her own volition or under the intense pressure from the priestess, I do not know, but when she called out, 'Enter Python,' she began to tremble with ecstasy and began to speak in a garbled, hysterical language. From that time on, her personality changed, and her depression, compounded by a guilty conscience, deepened.

"Herod was so surprised to see her in such a state that he said nothing, but simply stared. Kooza was not surprised; he had been carrying the burden of his wife's condition for a long time, trying to hide her problem. Often he made excuses for her, and often he covered up for her, but it was getting progressively worse. One of his friends happened to stumble into the truth and told him confidentially, 'You must face the fact that Joanna is going insane; you ought to send her away. If you try to keep her condition hidden here in Tiberias, sooner or later your dark secret will be discovered, and it will bring you down, too.

"Kooza was at a loss to know what to do. He could not send her away, but he knew of no one who could help her. He begged his friend to keep his secret, and tried to handle the problem by himself. Often Joanna could not sleep; terrifying nightmares would waken her, and she would lie on the bed stiff and trembling, afraid to go to sleep again lest the same dream would attack her. So Kooza and Joanna would walk the floor, hand in hand, most of the time in silence. When they did talk, it was Joanna lamenting and bemoaning her lost condition. 'I have invited this evil spirit into my bosom, and now it won t leave. He says I made a promise, and he is going to hold me to it. He says that if I call on my God Jehovah, he will torment me. I have tried to pray, but the heavens are as brass.'

"There was not much Kooza knew to say to her; his words of encouragement seemed so feeble against the power of the evil that had occupied her, body, soul, and spirit. He talked to her about the power of God, but she reminded him that when King Saul visited the Witch of Endor, it sealed his doom, and she was sure that she had committed an evil at least as great. Then Joanna would say, 'I am dragging you down with me. I must flee to the wilderness and die there before I destroy you.'

"It was then that Kooza realized that he would have to trust his secret to his house servant and count on him to keep watch over his wife while he was away. Somehow, that morning she had slipped out, and stood before Herod with a strange and frightening look in her eyes. She raised her hand, pointing to Herod and when she spoke, it did not sound like Joanna speaking; even Kooza did not recognize her voice. In a singsong way she intoned, 'Beware, beware of the sandstorm, the sandstorm of the desert. From the rocks, from the rocks it will come, and you will disappear in its treachery. Do not lose your seat in Tiberias.'

"Kooza put his arms around her and said, 'Come, come Joanna; I will take you home.' He was too embarrassed to look at Herod. If he had looked, he would have seen a terrified man. Just that morning, only a short time before his meeting with Kooza, a runner had arrived from the desert of Arabia — from the rock city of Petra — from King Aretas and the message he bore was a declaration of war! Joanna could know nothing of this! Was this God warning him of his doom? Fear gripped him; he would have to act quickly or he would be lost.

"It was true that Aretas had a real quarrel with Herod. Herod had married his daughter and was given a kingly dowry, but when Herodias seduced him it was the end of that relationship. Herod sent her home to her father, and she went back angry, bitter, disgraced. Aretas was very fond of his daughter and vowed that he would make Herod pay.

"And Aretas was a king to be reckoned with. If Herod had weighed this carefully, he would have been more diplomatic about what he did. Aretas was the fourth ruler in the line to bear that name, and he was the greatest of them all. His capital city, Petra, is the most remarkable city in the whole world — it is carved out of solid stone, beautiful stone in an array of soft colors, mostly rose red, but also pink and purple. The buildings that are carved into this stone are unbelievably beautiful — the Great High Place, the Temple of Winged Lions, the Theater. And what a place to defend! It is in a valley between two rock ridges, rising at least a thousand feet on either side, and it can be entered only by a narrow, winding cleft in the eastern ridge. A small band could hold off an army in that location.

"From this citadel, Aretas commanded a thousand desert outposts, controlling all the southern land routes to south Arabia, India, and even China. And Herod sat in Galilee with his meager resources! Aretas knew that and was making unreasonable demands for territory on the east side of the Salt Sea, territory that Herod did not want to give up, and under Roman law, had no right to give up. No wonder Herod was frightened!

"But let me come back to Joanna. As Kooza led her home, she was weeping hysterically, and quite loudly. Justin was not far off and, attracted by the noise, came over to investigate. Kooza was so distraught that he could no longer hold his secret, and told Justin the whole story. He did so, not because he thought Justin would help, but because he couldn't contain it any longer. To his amazement, Justin said, 'I know what you must do; I know who can help you.' Kooza was stunned. He had expected nothing, but here was a man speaking with such quiet confidence, and saying things that were unbelievable — saying that Joanna could be completely delivered.

"Justin told Kooza what I had shared with him after my assistant was healed. I had told him what the elder Ezra had told me about the man who had yelled out in the synagogue and was healed when Jesus commanded the evil spirit to come out. He also told Kooza how I had discerned that the power of God rested on Jesus of Nazareth so that he had authority to command, even as I command those under me, and his commands would be obeyed, and none could resist. He ended by saying, 'You must get her to Jesus!'

" 'But how?' asked Kooza.

" 'Don't worry,' replied Justin. 'My friend the Capernaum centurion can arrange everything.' And that's how I got involved.

"When I got the word from Justin, I went to see the fisherman Zebedee. I had met him on my first day in Capernaum, and I knew his two sons, James and John, who had been in the fishing business with their father, but now spent little time fishing; they spent their time with Jesus. When I told Zebedee about Joanna, he was happy to help — 'that's what Jesus came for' — he told me, and he suggested that I ask Sarah to help also.

"In a few days, Kooza and Joanna came to Capernaum and stayed with Alex and Sarah. That very evening, a crowd gathered around the house where Jesus was teaching, and one of Zebedee's sons, I think it was John, brought Joanna in to stand before Jesus. I don't know how to tell you this, but I will just tell you what they told me. When Jesus commanded the evil spirit to come out, the spirit answered him, and said he had been invited in and would not leave. But Jesus issued a command, and Joanna fell to the floor. Somebody cried out, 'She is dead!' But Jesus took her by the hand and lifted her up, and there she stood, praising God. That was years ago, and she has not had a bit of trouble since. In fact, she spent a good deal of her time following Jesus and his disciples. A number of women did this, and I know for a fact that they supplied the money so the group could survive. Now, I find that to be quite humorous — Herod's money going to support the ministry of Jesus whom he hated.

"And he did hate him! Whenever he heard of him, his guilty conscience was stirred, and he said, 'This is John the Baptist come back from the dead to haunt me.' He gave orders that Jesus should be killed if he ever set foot in Tiberias. When I heard of this, I passed the warning on to his disciples, but Jesus replied, 'Prophets are killed only in Jerusalem.' How prophetic that was!

"Back in Tiberias, Herod was agitated and fearful. He thought that

Aretas would seize the southern part of his territory, especially his palace at Mackus. In order to prepare for this eventuality, he decided to send an army to fortify that area. He called a council of war with Justin, the Roman centurion, Abner the commander of Herod's army, Kooza, and several of his close advisers. He spoke first to Justin: 'I will need the might of Rome to repel this attack,' he said, trying to sound like a forceful leader! but at the same time betraying his fear in his eyes. He should have been able to anticipate Justin's reply. 'I have no power to march into war. I do not have enough men, and my orders are to keep the peace in Galilee. Until they threaten the gates of Tiberias, I must stay at my post. I can send only eight men to bring back an official report to send to Rome.'

" 'Eight men!' shouted Herod in frustration. 'With all the desert hoards against me! What good will eight men do me? I know Caesar would help me.'

" 'I am sure that he would,' replied Justin. He was well aware of the friendship between Caesar Tiberius and Herod, and how much Herod had done to cultivate this friendship. 'But here's your problem — you will have to get a decree from Caesar himself, and then gather the Roman army. At this time of the year, communication takes time, and is uncertain. I would have to send a messenger to Caesar, have him find a ship sailing to Rome, see Caesar, and then make the return trip. That takes time.'

" 'Then it's up to you, Abner,' said Herod, trying to shift the responsibility. Abner was about to say, 'Who? Me?' but then he thought better of it. It would do no good, and would make him appear weak and timid. Instead he said, 'What do you suggest that I do?'

"Herod had thought about this, so he said, 'You must raise an army from all Galilee; they will be willing to fight to protect their lands. Then go to my brother Philip and get whatever help he is willing to give. Get as many men as you can; appeal to their national pride, call for men of courage. Then let us hope that God will be on our side.'

"That last part was the sticking point. When Abner came to Capernaum to beg for recruits and quoted Herod's, 'Let us hope that God will be on our side,' the crowd hooted in derision. Someone shouted, 'God left him the night he killed John the Baptist.' An old man stood and said, 'Herod is doomed; he will die by the sword of the Arabs.' This discouraged Abner, and when he left Capernaum, he had recruited only a small ragtag band of malcontents. And he didn't do much better in the other towns of

Galilee.

"When he went to Herod Philip's territory, the response was better. This encouraged him, but it should have alerted him that something was out of order. Why should these men, so far removed, be so anxious to join the army? If Abner gave this any thought, it was only a moment; he needed all the men he could get.

"Upon returning to Tiberias, he learned something that did not cheer his heart — Herod decided not to go into battle himself; the whole responsibility was on his shoulders. This decision had begun to form in Herod's mind when Joanna had made her hysterical prophecy; he could not get this out of his mind. Then one night he had a terrifying dream: He was trapped in the dungeon in the Mackus palace, the very dungeon that had held John the Baptist, and both John and Aretas were advancing on him with drawn swords. When he awoke from the dream, he vowed that he would never go to that palace again. Now it appeared that the palace might be the center of the conflict.

" 'You're nothing but a coward!' Herodias taunted him. 'What will your men think if you are afraid to go?'

" 'I don't care what the men think,' retorted Herod. 'I don't want to die at the hands of the Arabs.'

" 'It's all in your mind,' replied Herodias. 'Are you going to let the words of an insane woman govern your life?'

"But Herod would not be moved. It troubled him, kept him awake nights, and occupied all his thoughts. One day he said to himself, 'I wonder if Joanna has a new and better prophecy for me.' So he called for Kooza and asked him to bring his wife along. Joanna almost refused to go, but there seemed to be no way to avoid the meeting without a real conflict. When they arrived, it was obvious that Herod was agitated, fearing the worst, wanting to know, but at the same time, not wanting to know. So he blurted out, 'Give me another prophecy, and make it a good one this time!'

"Before Joanna could reply, Kooza put his arm around her and said quietly, 'The evil spirit that troubled Joanna is no longer in her. She has been delivered, and she cannot even remember what she said to you last time.'

" 'So it was an evil spirit, was it?' roared Herod. 'Then how did it know I was being threatened from the desert? Answer me that!'

" 'I cannot, my Lord,' replied Kooza,' I do not understand these things. I only know that when Jesus of Nazareth commanded it to leave her, she was set free and hasn't been troubled since.'

" 'Can't she tell me anything? Was the prophecy true?' asked Herod, desperately seeking some direction for his troubled life.

" 'Only God knows the future,' replied Kooza. 'We cannot help you.'

" 'Then leave!' ordered Herod. 'You are no good to me.'

"This solidified his resolve. Nothing would make him leave Tiberias to go to battle. 'I will not die in the desert,' he muttered to himself.

"Abner finally got his army together and marched off. Let me tell you, it did not look like a Roman army. Even in practice drills, we demand absolute precision. They looked more like a flock of ragged sheep, and as it turned out, they were sheep being led to slaughter. Off they marched, but not with confidence. Some of Herod's fear had rubbed off on Abner, and although some of the men exhibited some excitement at this adventure, the eight Romans Justin had sent along feared for their lives.

"The disaster came from an unexpected quarter. Aretas did not come with his troops, and there was never a chance to determine if his generals could have defeated Herod's forces in an even fight. There was no even fight; the men recruited from Philip's territory had planned all along to see to it that Herod suffered a defeat. When the Arabians attacked from the front, Philip's men attacked from the rear, and Herod's so-called army ran in every direction in utter confusion. Abner had taken a position on a hill to be able to see the battle and direct his forces, and it was fortunate for him that he did, or he would have been lost in the slaughter. The eight Romans fought their way through the melee with only superficial injuries, but most of the army was mowed down like grass. Before the battle was over, Philip's men melted away and presumably made their way back home. Philip denied any knowledge of them or complicity in their actions. Abner eventually returned home with a handful of demoralized men.

"When Abner gave his report to Herod, he was furious and threatened revenge against everyone in sight. He talked of putting Abner and the survivors to death for cowardice, until his own conscience reminded him that he was the biggest coward of all. When the centurion Justin entered the conference, the whole matter changed. Justin was grim. 'This matter is now a concern of Caesar,' he said in stern tones. And then, turning to Herod, he said, 'You can be sure that Caesar will not rest until this affront to the Roman empire has been avenged. Aretas is as good as dead! His kingdom will be destroyed. I promise you this in the name of

Tiberius.'

"Justin had judged the response of Tiberius accurately. It did take time for the message to arrive in Rome, but the response was swift and sure. He did not order the small Roman force in Israel to do the job, but instead, wrote to Vitellius, legate to Syria and the highest Roman official in that part of the world, and ordered him to assemble an overwhelming force. He said, 'Bring Aretas bound to Rome so I can parade him through the streets in dishonor, or else, just bring me his head.'

"Vitellius did this at once. He gathered together two legions — ten thousand men, and the cavalry, and the support forces from the best of all the nearby kingdoms, and they came marching from Damacus in Roman precision, with banners and ensigns, a glorious, irresistible force. Now it was Aretas's turn to be worried. When word reached him that the Roman army was advancing with orders to annihilate him he did not know which way to turn. So, like so many others, he turned to his soothsayers to ask for advice. They told him, 'Don't worry, the Romans will never set foot in Petra.' This seemed most unlikely, but at least it was not an evil prophecy, and since he did not know what else to do, he did nothing. It seemed that Herod was about to be avenged of his humiliation .

"When the Jewish religious leaders heard that the Roman army was at their border and intended to march through to Arabia, they were horrified. You see, the Roman ensigns contained images of the Roman gods, and the Jews did not want these heathen gods marching through their holy land, even if it was to fight their enemy. The leaders rushed to Ptolemaïs, on the coast of the Great Sea just north of Sidon, and they begged Vitellius not to pass through their land with the idols. But the Roman soldiers would not go without their images to protect them. Vitellius told the leaders that he had orders from Caesar and had to obey, but they produced an agreement from Tiberius saying that Roman idols would not be forced on them, so there they stood. Vitellius could not turn back — he had orders to bring in Aretas dead or alive. He could not go forward — Tiberius had agreed to respect the religious wishes of the Jews.

"Herod appeared on the scene, afraid that he would be the loser, and Aretas would remain a thorn in his side. Something had to be done! Then they reached a compromise; the army would have to march all the way around the border of Israel to the Great Plain. Herod and Vitellius went to Jerusalem to wait until the army had made its long circuitous journey.

On the fourth day news arrived that changed it all — Tiberius had died — and Vitellius was ordered immediately to take an oath of allegiance to the new Caesar, Caligula. This he did.

" 'What does this mean for my battle?' asked Herod nervously.

" 'Your battle is off!' responded Vitellius. 'Orders given by Tiberius are meaningless now. I have no choice but to disband the army and send them home.'

"The Roman gods on the ensigns had saved Aretas, and Herod was disappointed again. But the elder Ezra said to me, 'God is against Herod, and even when he calls on the might of Rome to help him, he cannot succeed, and you will see that there is more judgment to come.'

"Ezra was right."

6

The next time Livy came to talk with Castor, he found him sitting in his garden enjoying the sun that was just breaking through the morning fog that filled the valley. He looked like a picture of peace and serenity, and Livy hated to disturb him with more prosaic matters. He paused in the path, but Castor had heard him coming, and said, "Here, my young friend, come sit beside me and let us talk."

Livy came and sat on the bench facing him and said, "You looked so peaceful that I did not want to break into your reverie. After your active life, I think you are entitled to some peace and quiet."

"I appreciate your concern," replied Castor, "But as a matter of fact, I was trying to collect my thoughts and figure out how we should proceed today. The death of Tiberius made many changes for many people, and I am wondering which path to follow."

"You are doing a good job," said Livy. "This is the kind of material I need for my history. I never knew that a Roman army had ever marched to make war against Petra. That's the kind of thing I want — the interplay between Israel and Rome."

"I'm glad you're writing this," said Castor. "There is a story here that most people know nothing about, and it seems that everything that happened in Israel had the stamp of Rome upon it. Now I don't know what to tell you next. The death of Tiberius interrupted Herod's plans. Should I continue with his story?" Castor paused and thought for a moment. "No, I can't. His path crossed that of Pontius Pilate, and Pilate's plans were interrupted by the death of Tiberius also. But I ought to tell you about Agrippa, because he was affected most by Tiberius's death, and ended up with the territories of both Herod and Pilate. It is a tangled web, but I will have to start somewhere."

Livy frowned and said, "I am a Roman, and you would think I would know all about Tiberius, but I was just a lad when he died. Perhaps you ought to give me a little background on him so I can make the pieces fit."

44

"Good idea!" said Castor. "I don't suppose you could understand the events in Israel without understanding the odd quirks of his personality. Let me give you a little background on this strange man who ruled the Roman Empire for twenty-two years, and in a way, affected everyone who lived in it.

"I saw him once. It was a triumphal march up the Via Sacra. In his uniform, he looked every bit the emperor — broad shoulders, powerful arms. I noticed especially his large, expressive eyes. And one other thing — he was left handed. His father had been an officer under Julius Caesar, and after his father's death, his wife, Libia, married Caesar Augustus. She had ambitions for her young son, and made sure that he got good appointments. Perhaps he didn't need this kind of help, because he was very talented, and won some brilliant military campaigns in Gaul, and thus, made a name for himself.

"But Augustus was the kind of man who liked to run everyone's life, and he did not like the wife Tiberius had married, so he ordered him to divorce her and marry his daughter, Julia. Tiberius did not want to do this; he loved his wife, and hated his stepsister, Julia, but he had no choice; one could not argue with the emperor. Caesar could force him to marry Julia, but he could not force him to love her, and he didn't.

"In a short time, he left her and went to live in Rhodes. In a couple of years, he returned to Rome to take charge of the army, and in time, Augustus took him back into his good graces. I think he did this because he had no one to follow him and take over the empire. When Augustus died, Tiberius was proclaimed Caesar.

"He started off well, following the conservative policies of Augustus, and Rome certainly prospered financially, but Tiberius could not get along with the senate and the ruling class in Rome. They wanted a say in the government and complained that Tiberius never consulted them, never listened to their suggestions, and often deliberately antagonized them. They fought and quarreled, and finally great Caesar got tired of it all, gave up, and went to live in Capri.

"He left the captain of the Praetorian guard in charge of his interests. The man's name was Sejanus. Tiberius thought he could trust him, but that was a mistake. While Tiberius was basking in the sun in Capri, Sejanus was carrying out a reign of terror in Rome, and he set about to eliminate anyone who would be a challenge to him. The list of those he murdered included Tiberius's only son, and his nephew. When Tiberius heard of this, he ordered Sejanus killed, and vowed that he would never trust anyone again. He became suspicious of everyone, and for the slightest excuse, or for no excuse at all, he had them eliminated. Now keep that in mind while I tell you about Pilate and Jesus of Nazareth.

"One morning I went to Zebedee's house to get some fish. There is no fish market in Capernaum, but each fisherman has a room in his house that is used as a shop. I found Zebedee sitting on a bench outside his shop, so I sat down to talk. Soon the conversation turned to politics; it often did. I must confess that usually I started it because I wanted to understand the thinking of the people, and Zebedee was a simple but astute man, and was a good soundingboard. In the conversation, he was complaining about Rome again, and I asked him, 'How can you complain against Rome when the ruler of Galilee is a Jew?'

" 'You may call him a Jew, but I don't. He is only part Jew, part Idumean, and remember this — he was raised in Rome and completely adopted Roman ways. But he is not as bad as Pilate, and as for Pilate ...' Here Zebedee thought of spitting on the ground to show his disgust, but I suppose, out of deference to me, he did not. 'Pilate has no use for the Jews at all, and I am sure that Tiberius has told him to oppress the Jews in order to keep us from rebelling.'

"I smiled at him and said, 'You must admit that the Jews have never been model citizens. You have given Rome trouble from the beginning.'

" 'True,' said Zebedee, stroking his beard. Because of our religion, we never will be. We bow the knee only to Jehovah, and His laws are the only laws we truly accept. We pay our Temple tax, but the tax to Caesar will always be a sore point with us. You see, it implies allegiance to him. Our lawyers are always arguing about this. If the Temple tax is an act of worship, then giving tax to Caesar is also an act of worship. According to some, we should die rather than pay.'

" 'And you know, Zebedee, how Rome would treat that — you would die!' I said, knowing that he knew that too.

"Zebedee continued: 'My son James told me that the leaders in Jerusalem tried to put Jesus in this impossible position when they asked him to answer — yes or no — should we pay tribute to Caesar? Emotions were charged. The people wanted him to say, "No!" Who wants to pay taxes? But more than that, it is an affront to our national identity; it reminds us that we are a conquered people. Any popular leader would be against this. But if Jesus had said no, they would have gone to Pilate immediately to report it. James told me what happened: Jesus reached into his purse for a coin, and finding none, he asked, "Does someone have a penny?" One of the Pharisees produced a coin, and Jesus took it and looked at it for a while, and then asked, almost innocently — as though he didn't know — "Whose image is this?" Of course they answered, "Caesar Tiberius." Then pointing to the words on the coin, "Whose inscription is this?" Again they said, "Caesar's." Then Jesus said something I have heard repeated many times. He said, "Render unto Caesar the things that are Caesar's, and unto God the things that are God's." '

"I replied to him, 'I agree with that. You have peace and tranquillity here in Capernaum because I am here to enforce the law; it is only fair that you help to pay my salary.'

" 'If I had been taxed only to pay your salary, I would be a rich man by now. Paying taxes to Rome is like pouring water down a hole in the ground; you pour and pour, but the hole is never full. I am a good Jew, and I am your friend, but I will tell you that it hurts me to pay my taxes. That is why that question put Jesus in such a tight spot.'

"I ought to make it clear, Livy, that Pilate would not have been sympathetic to anyone who advocated withholding taxes because he knew that Tiberius would look on that as rebellion. On top of that, Tiberius was becoming anti-Jewish. Part of this sprang from his growing paranoia, but a particular incident confirmed his warped suspicion that Jews were dangerous to the Roman empire.

"I reminded Zebedee of the doings of a man named Simeon who had passed through Capernaum some years before. He appeared in the synagogues with three friends and passed himself off as a traveling teacher of the law. Zebedee responded, 'Yes, and he was a good teacher. He knew the law by heart, and his explanations and illustrations were excellent. I thought he was a master, and perhaps, he was. But he was also a master thief!' "

Castor smiled to himself as he remembered how angry Zebedee had been as he said those last words. Then he said to Livy, "I investigated him. After gaining the confidence of the people, Simeon told them that he was taking a special offering to the Temple in Jerusalem, and he urged them all to contribute to it. In an emotional speech, he told them that God honored only true sacrifice of the best, the finest, and if they would give their best, God would open the windows of heaven upon them. The people heaped their treasures on him. Well, needless to say, Simeon and his friends soon disappeared, and the treasures with them, and nothing ever got to the Temple. When the elder Ezra came to me with the story,

I passed it on through the centurion network, and found that this had been Simeon's pattern for a long time. When we caught him in Caesarea, we put him on a ship and deported him. We thought that was the end of the problem, but it wasn't.

"Simeon and his three friends went to Rome, and soon found themselves without money, and since they were unwilling to work, they came up with a new plan — they held classes for wealthy women who wanted to learn about the Jewish religion. Such a thing, I would think, would be a losing proposition in a place like Rome, but they did get their hooks into one noble woman named Fulvia, and they began getting money from her. When they came up with their 'gifts for the Temple' ruse, she loaded them down with purple and gold.

"All this time, her husband, Saturn, was most unhappy with his wife's involvement, but he figured she was bored and would soon lose interest in this latest amusement and go on to something else. However, when she let it slip that she had parted with a small fortune for the Temple project, he investigated it, and learned all about these men. He then went to Tiberius who mumbled something about 'scheming Jews,' and not only issued a decree banishing Simeon and his three friends, but also four thousand innocent Jews who knew nothing about this matter. Pilate was well aware of this and of Caesar's attitudes, and knew that he would be in favor of firm control in Judea. But let me come back to the Jews and Jesus.

"The leaders decided that they had to do away with Jesus. In part, they feared that the great following he had would give Rome the excuse it needed to come in and completely subjugate the nation. I can tell you that Tiberius had considered this because he no longer trusted the Jews. But the real reason was that Jesus was an outsider, not a part of the power structure, the ruling group, and he was a threat to their positions. They had religious differences with him, but these were minor when compared with the arguments between themselves; they could agree on almost nothing! One thing they could agree on — if anyone claimed to be the Son of God, that was blasphemy worthy of death. Jesus made this claim. He also claimed to be King of the Jews according to their ancient prophecies of a golden age of peace, but they were sure that Tiberius would see this as a present threat and a direct challenge to him. So they had him!

"Pilate had no love for the Jewish leaders — they were a thorn in his side — and to them, he was the enemy. Some said that Pilate had once told a friend that he was sent there to destroy the Jewish religion, and it appeared that he enjoyed tormenting the Jews. He knew what they thought about the Roman ensigns and idols; still, he brought them from Caesarea secretly by night and set them up in Jerusalem. What a stir that made! He finally removed them, but he had made many enemies. Another time, he hung golden shields with images right in the Temple. He claimed he was doing this to honor Caesar, and it is my opinion that he would do anything to curry favor with Caesar. When the people complained about the shields, he sent in the soldiers and slaughtered quite a number of them while they were sacrificing."

Livy interrupted and said, "I can see why the Jews were distressed with Roman rule. Did you know Pilate? He must have been a contemporary of yours in Rome."

"I didn't know him well," said Castor. "Yes, he was in Rome when I was, but he was from a wealthy family, the Pontius family, and we moved in different circles. I went into the army, and his father sent him to school to study government administration. In those days, he had a fierce temper, and one night he got into a fight and killed a man. His father intervened for him, and for punishment, he was sent to Bithynia to a remote post among rebellious tribes. Believe it or not, he did an excellent job, perhaps because of his harshness, and that was what put him in line for the post in Judea. He got into trouble when he treated the Jews like he treated the barbarians.

"Pilate had his royal residence at Caesarea, a beautiful city built by Herod the Great, with a magnificent man-made harbor, the largest of the Great Sea, and beautiful buildings to rival any city in the world. He had come to Jerusalem at Passover time, because, if there was going to be trouble, it would probably come at Passover. Now let me tell you what Maxus, the Roman centurion told me.

"They roused Pilate early in the morning. He did not like this. He had been up late the night before, and this added to his foul mood. He went to meet the chief priests and leaders in the Fortress of Antonia where he had his judgment seat. When he saw that they had gotten him out of bed early to deal with an argument about religion, he was annoyed and considered throwing them all out. They began to bring their accusations against Jesus, but Pilate broke in and said, 'I don't want to hear any of this! I don't know about your religious laws, and I don't want to know!'

"But they were not going to let this go; they had gone to a great deal of trouble already, and they were going to see it through. The temple guards had arrested Jesus late the night before before, and the religious leaders had held their trial in the High Priest's palace. They had concluded that he was guilty of blasphemy against the Temple and guilty because he claimed to be Christ, the Son of God. Now they had brought him bound to Pilate, and they demanded his death. Pilate tried to reason with them, but one cannot reason with a mob hungry for blood. Pilate sensed the situation and tried to avoid getting caught in the middle. 'What evil has he done?' he demanded. One of the priests cried out, 'He is stirring up rebellion from Galilee to Jerusalem.' Galilee? Pilate saw a glimmer of hope: 'Is he from Galilee? That is out of my jurisdiction; that's Herod's problem. Take him to Herod, and let him settle this.'

"Herod was in Jerusalem for the Passover; he always came for the Passover, and half of Tiberias with him. Capernaum was like a ghost town with so many gone.

"Those who were followers of Jesus traveled in a group, and this group included Zebedee and his wife, Salome, Sarah and Alex, and down the road at Tiberias, Joanna joined them, although Kooza had to stay behind to keep the wheels turning in Tiberias.

"Herod had a palace in Jerusalem, the ancient Maccabean palace, and it was here that the priests and leaders brought Jesus. You will remember that I told you that Herod had threatened Jesus, and although Jesus had ministered throughout Galilee for over three years, Herod had never laid eyes on him. When he heard that the leaders were bringing Jesus to him for a verdict, he was happy about this. He gathered his soldiers together in the great hall, put on his regal robes, and waited for them to arrive. He said to one of his men, 'Now we will see if this man is a fake or if he really is a miracleworker. He is going to have to perform a miracle — a real one — to get out of this!'

"When Jesus arrived amid the tumult of the crowd, he looked worn and appeared to have been mistreated. The conversation with Herod was definitely one-sided, Jesus would not say a word. 'Do a miracle!' demanded Herod. 'Do it, or you are finished!' Jesus stood there motionless, a picture of serenity and dignity in the midst of a rising tide of anger and hate. They all mocked him, ridiculed him, and abused him with foul language.

"When it was over, Herod called the High Priest aside and said to him, 'I do not have the power of death over him now that he is in the hands of Rome. If you want him crucified, you will have to take him back to Pilate.' The High Priest knew this was true, so he said, 'Give us a decree to take to Pilate saying that he ought to be put to death for the good of Rome.' Herod retired to his room and soon returned with a parchment sealed with his seal and gave it to the High Priest. What the High Priest did not know was that Herod had written, 'He is not worthy of death; he has broken no Roman laws.'

"Back to Pilate they went, but he was not happy to have this problem back in his lap. By now he could see that the only thing that would satisfy the crowd was the crucifixion of this man that he himself had declared innocent. That was not the Roman way! Pilate muttered, 'I would rather crucify the whole bunch of those religious leaders; they make nothing but trouble for me.'

"And there was another complication — Pilate's wife, Procula. I met her once before she married Pilate, and I was impressed with her. I suppose one could say she was beautiful, with even features and long, flowing hair, but I was more impressed by her gentle spirit and friendly smile.

"Her family was quite poor, and when Pilate took an interest in her, her father saw this as a chance to make a good match, which would benefit both Procula and himself. I heard that Procula was not happy with the arrangement, but like a good daughter, she went along with it. I am sure she did not have an easy life, and even though I am a confirmed bachelor at heart, I couldn't help thinking that she would have had a better life with me than with Pilate. His harsh treatment of others bothered her, and she tried by gentle persuasion, to change his attitudes. But he took this as criticism, and that was one thing he would not tolerate. So Procula had to stand aside while Pilate went his way, stepping on people. When the matter with Jesus came up, she could no longer remain silent.

"Pilate was in the midst of the shouting and accusations when Procula came to the judgment hall and sent a servant in with a message saying that she had to see Pilate at once. He came out to see her, unhappy at her interruption, still, happy to leave the unpleasantness of the business, at least for a short time .

" 'What do you want?' he said, his voice spilling out all the frustration and anger that had been building up within him. 'Didn't I tell you never to bother me when I am busy?'

" 'This is important, Pilate; you must listen to me! It's about Jesus!' she said with great urgency.

" 'What about him?' snapped Pilate.

"Emotion filled Procula's voice as she said, 'Oh, Pilate, do not have anything to do with that just man. Release him! Let him go! He is more than a man; he is the Christ, the Son of God!'

"Pilate stiffened with fear. That was what the chief priests were saying. Could this be true? But his wife was still speaking, telling of the dream she had just had. '... and in my dream, I saw you strike Jesus in the face, and he fell to the floor at your judgment seat, and blood began to cover the floor. You lifted your feet to get them out of the blood, and ... you put your feet on Jesus! Then you looked at your hands, and they were dripping with blood. When I saw your face, I was filled with fear for you, and I began to shake. Then there was a rumble like an earthquake, and a pit opened before you, and you fell into it screaming. Then I woke up. Pilate! Let him go!'

"I should tell you, Livy, that it was more than that dream that made Procula feel that way. She had heard Jesus speak one day in Jerusalem, and something had happened within her. Procula had been walking near the Temple when she saw a large group of people gathered around Jesus, listening intently to what he had to say. She didn't hear much, only the last part, but what she heard convinced her that she had to hear more. Jesus was saying, 'If anyone is thirsty, let him come to me and I will give living water that will be like a bubbling spring within him, and it will bubble up into everlasting life.'

"Procula understood at once what he was saying. If anyone was thirsting for meaning, for reality, it was Procula. She felt isolated in a foreign country; Pilate had shut her out of his life, and nothing she did seemed to have meaning any longer. Desperately, desperately, she longed for a bubbling spring within her, and even the thought that this might be possible created a surge of anticipation. Perhaps there was an answer to life, after all. Of course, she could not share any of this with Pilate; she could not share even trivial concerns with him; how could she share this when she knew that he would immediately disapprove?

"But Pilate was speaking, and that brought her back into the present. He was speaking in anger, but she knew that the anger had been boiling before she had spoken to him. 'You don't understand!' he was saying. 'Nobody understands!' Then he left the room and went back to the crowd.

"Pilate held up his hands for silence, and when there was quiet, he said, 'I have decided what I will do. I will have him whipped as a warning, and then let him go.'

"This inflamed the crowd, and they began to chant, louder and louder, with increasing intensity, 'Crucify him! Crucify him! Crucify him!'

" 'Shall I crucify your king?' asked Pilate.

" 'We have no king but Caesar! We have no king but Caesar!' shouted the crowd. The High Priest raised his arms for silence, and then said sternly and solemnly, 'This man has committed treason against Caesar Tiberius by proclaiming himself a king and amassing a large following. If you let him go, we will present a formal charge against you to Caesar, proclaiming that you are an enemy of Caesar.' At this, the crowd roared and shouted until it seemed that they would never stop. In the midst of the noise, Pilate did a dramatic thing; he called for a basin of water, and then slowly, deliberately, he washed his hands saying, 'I hereby wash my hands of this whole matter; his blood is on your heads.'

" 'So be it!' shouted the crowd, 'on us and on our children.' I tell you the truth, Livy, I tremble for them every time I think of that. I believe that will come true in ways that they could never imagine.

"So they crucified him," said Castor slowly. Then he paused, and Livy was not sure that he was going to continue.

"Next time," said Livy. "That's enough for today."

"But there's more to the story," protested Castor.

"I'm sure there is," said Livy. "Collect your thoughts, and we will pick it up again next time."

7

Livy left his home and briskly walked down the road to Castor's villa. He opened the gate and started up the walk and was pleasantly surprised when Castor came to greet him with a hearty handshake and a ready smile. "I greet you on this fine morning, my young historian," said Castor. Livy was relieved to find him in such an exuberant mood. because after their last session, he had seemed drained and exhausted. Livy wondered if he was putting too much pressure on the old centurion.

"Forgive me for saying this," began Livy, "but when you were telling me about what happened to Jesus last time, you seemed to be very emotionally involved."

"I was — I am," said Castor, "for several reasons, although I was not there. This is another case of the twisted threads of history. The Roman centurion, Maxus, was in charge of executions, and I have known him since we were rookies in the same cohort many years ago. He told me that a little distance from the crucifixion site, there was a group of broken-hearted watchers, and they were friends of mine, too: Sarah and Alex, Joanna, Zebedee and his wife Salome, and of course, I also knew Zebedee's sons and Peter. I was sitting home in Capernaum enjoying the peace and quiet, not knowing that they were going through the most traumatic times of their lives. It was only when Sarah and Alex returned and hurried to see me that I learned anything about the events, and the story came out in bits and pieces with such excitement that I had to stop many times to remind them that they were telling the end of the story before explaining the middle. I didn't see Maxus until a year later, so it took me some time to put things together, and even now, the story is so interwoven that it is hard to tell it all in one piece.

"As I said, Sarah and Alex came to me with great excitement, and even before our greetings were over, Sarah blurted out, 'Jesus was crucified!' This news stunned me! I had feared as much, because I knew Pilate did not tolerate any challenge to his power, and I knew of the antagonism of the religious leaders. But I was more than stunned — I was profoundly puzzled. If this was true, why wasn't Sarah devastated with grief? I could not accept what she was saying because of the way she was saying it. I held up my hand and said to her, 'Wait, wait; how can you tell me that news without being overcome with grief?'

"Sarah fairly shouted with joy, 'But he is alive!'

"Now I was truly confused. It had to be one way or the other — it couldn't be both — so I said to her, 'You had better start at the beginning and take it one step at a time.'

"Sarah began her story: 'We were watching from a distance ... we didn't want to see the terrible thing, and yet we did. It was awful, and much of the time I stood there with my eyes closed, praying to God for deliverance. I thought deliverance would surely come, but it didn't. And our grief was mocked by the scorn of the crowd. You would think there would have been some pity, some sign of human compassion; but there was none. And the priests, the men who were supposed to speak for God ... they taunted him, laughed at him, called on him to come down from the cross.'

" 'There were two other men crucified with him, and they joined in. One of them had a loud, boisterous voice, and his language was crude and his words dripping with sarcasm. "Save yourself and us, if you are so great!" I listened and then said to myself, "That voice ... it sounds familiar. Could it be?" I said to Alex, " Go up closer and see if that man is missing a middle finger." "Missing a middle finger?" Alex asked me in astonishment. "What do you mean?" I said to him, "That loud man is Kish, the man who captured me on the road to Jericho!" Alex went up close enough to see, and came back nodding his head; it was! But I could not feel happy about that. It was an awful thing to do to any man, no matter how bad he was. You can imagine, if I felt that about the evil man who had wronged me, how I felt about Jesus who was suffering so.' "

Castor sank back on his seat as though he were feeling the grief that Sarah had spoken of. He had not been there, but he had seen men crucified before, and even though he had seen death in battle, this was different. It was not only the suffering, but the fact that the suffering was made to be a public spectacle, a gruesome amusement. What lasting marks would this leave on a tender woman like Sarah?

Castor continued his story and said, "Perhaps this is the place to tell you what my friend Maxus told me. To him, it was just part of his job, a very unpleasant part, but strange to say, his heart was moved with compassion for the man on the center cross. Something was different here; he was not like other men who suffered such a fate. He prayed, prayed for those who were doing this to him. When the sky grew dark at noon Maxus was sure his appraisal of this man was right. When he said his last words, they were like a shout of triumph, and he died, as though he had willed his spirit to leave his body. And then there was an earthquake! Maxus said to me, 'Surely that man was the Son of God!'

"Sarah and her friends did not know what would happen next, but they were determined to see this to the end. They had brought along a shroud for the body in case they would have a chance to use it. They had little hope, because the obstacles they faced were enormous, and they were afraid that the precious body would simply be thrown in the city dump as a final insult. In time, a man they did not know, evidently a rich man, came with some official papers and showed them to Maxus who ordered the soldiers to take the body down. Several times Sarah heard him say to the soldiers, 'Gently, gently.' This surprised her, and led her to believe they would be permitted to perform their labor of love. The man with the papers readily agreed, and the sorrowing procession went to a nearby garden and laid the body in a new tomb. Then, because it was the Sabbath, they went home to wait for the dawning of the first day of the week.

"The group from Capernaum had planned to leave for home early on the first day of the week, but Joanna and Zebedee's wife said they would not leave until they had finished anointing the body with spices according to their custom. Consequently, they started for the tomb while it was still dark and found that the stone had been rolled away, and the tomb was empty!"

It was obvious that Livy was skeptical at this point, and he immediately thought, *Surely there is some other explanation*. He voiced this by saying, "Perhaps they went to the wrong tomb."

"No, I don't think so," said Castor. "Sarah was quite sure at this point; the shroud that had been wrapped around the body was still there."

"That's not evidence enough for me," said Livy. His training as an historian was clearly showing.

Castor said, "But there is more!" After he had said that, he had second thoughts. Livy would most likely refute what he had to say. Livy waited for his words, so Castor felt constrained to continue. "There was an angel ..." Castor looked at his feet, shifting them back and forth, avoiding the unbelieving gaze of Livy.

"And what did the angel say?" asked Livy, not with obvious sarcasm, but certainly in complete unbelief.

Castor was not sure he wanted to continue this discussion because he could understand how this sounded, and indeed, would sound to any reasonable man. But he had started and had to finish; so he said, "The angel said Jesus came back from the dead and would see them in Galilee."

"And did they see him in Galilee?" asked Livy with raised eyebrows.

"Yes, they did, and I think I did also," replied Castor.

"You *think* you did?" asked Livy. "I should think you would know for sure if you had seen a man who came back from the dead after being crucified. Tell me about it."

Castor lifted his eyes and looked off into the distance; he waited a while before he continued. Then he said, "One morning shortly after that, just before sunrise, I went down to the lake to take a morning walk. A little way from me, I saw Zebedee's boat with six or seven men in it, and I remember thinking, 'It looks like the men are back fishing.' Zebedee's sons and Peter had given up the fishing business to follow Jesus; however, I was not surprised to see them back because I figured that was all over now. The only thing that surprised me was the huge net full of fish they were pulling in. Then I saw one man — later I learned that it was Peter — jump into the water and swim the short way to shore. On the shore I saw another man tending a small fire. Nothing unusual about that — just someone getting things ready for breakfast. I made the turn in the path, and they were no longer in view. I continued my walk and went home. Later that day, Zebedee told me that Jesus had met with some of his disciples by the lake, and then I thought again about what I had seen and mentioned it to Zebedee. 'That man on the shore, that man by the fire, that man was Jesus!' He looked like just another man to me, so when I saw him, it made no special impression on me, but I have thought about it many times since, I can tell you!"

"So you think it was Jesus?" said Livy.

"Yes, I do," replied Castor. "That's what Zebedee said, and I know I can trust him, and his sons certainly would not tell him something that was not true."

Livy thought about that for a while and then replied, "Here's what I must do, Castor; I will record faithfully what you have told me, but I will make no comment about it. After all, this is to be a political history, not a book of religion. I would have to have a great deal more information to make any kind of judgment on a matter as weighty as this, and even if I had all the information I needed, I doubt that anyone reading this in a book would be persuaded of such an impossible thing."

"Fair enough," replied Castor. "I will have to touch this matter again as different paths cross, but that is good enough for now. I really want to get back to the main thread, which is the strange union between Rome and Israel. In a way, it was symbolized when Pilate went to visit Herod, and the two became friends. But let that wait until next time, because I have a lot to tell about Pilate's history."

8

The day was not a pleasant one in which to take a walk, unless one enjoyed walking in a dripping rain that couldn't make up its mind whether to come down in earnest or give up the proposition altogether. The benches along the sides of the walk where Livy and Castor usually held their sessions were covered with puddles and Castor was nowhere in sight, so Livy assumed that the history lesson would be held indoors. He went to the wide door and lifted the heavy bronze knocker that was shaped like a lion, a regal lion showing its large teeth. He dropped it gently and was surprised that such a gentle knock should reverberate so loudly inside the house. He was simply being polite, not wishing to disturb Castor if he should be involved in more important affairs.

It was true, however, that Livy was in awe of Castor — mostly admiration but also a little intimidation. He had been thinking about their relationship. Castor seemed genuinely to like him; at times he thought that Castor might look upon him as the son he never had. But no one would ever take Livy for Castor's son. Castor was a large, powerful man; Livy was slim and not quite average in height. Castor's strong voice and dominant personality, the personality that made him a leader of men, was in stark contrast to the thin voice and overly careful diction of Livy, and Livy did not aspire to be a leader of anything. In the presence of Castor, Livy felt even smaller.

This history task meant a great deal to him, so he continued even though he thought he had no right to impose on Castor and to ask so much of his time for his selfish purpose. Once or twice he tried to talk to his father about this, but his father simply replied, "Nonsense! He is enjoying this as much as you are. He has a story to tell, and you are a good listener. He will be as pleased as you are with the outcome." So here he was again, with his wax tablets and stylus at Castor's door.

He did not have to wait long. Although Castor was retired, he lived by a careful schedule with a time and a place for everything. "It gives me the security of a well-ordered life." Castor always said. "The man with-

59

out a schedule is like a ship without a rudder." Certainly Castor was not a rudderless ship.

Castor opened the door, greeted Livy warmly, and conducted him into the library. The walls of the room were lined with cases holding scrolls, most of which bore titles dealing with military campaigns and Roman history. It was a comfortable room, a retreat from the dampness and drizzle of the day outside, and the warm air from the vents was especially welcome to Livy who felt chilled to the bone. He almost mentioned this to Castor, but caught himself because he did not want to appear to be a weakling before this man who had endured the worst weather in the field in the service of Rome. Castor brought over a small desk and placed it in front of Livy, and then took a step backward surveying the scene and said, "There — that's the way it should be. The historian seated at the desk in the library, ready to write for all posterity the dealings of Rome in the far corners of the empire."

Livy felt slightly embarrassed because he did not consider himself worthy of the title *historian*, at least not yet, and he wondered if Castor was saying this to humor him, but when he looked into Castor's face, he concluded that he was serious. Perhaps his father was right; perhaps Castor was as much involved in this as he was.

"So we take up Pilate again today?" asked Livy as Castor readied himself in the chair opposite him.

"Yes, Pilate," responded Castor, "but I don't think I can tell the whole story today, but let me start.

"Shortly after the crucifixion of Jesus, Pilate sent a messenger to Herod's palace. The Tiberias centurion, Justin, was standing just inside the gate when he arrived with a flourish and made his announcement, standing outside the gate and proclaiming his message like a royal decree, and I suppose it was. The message was brief and to the point: 'Prepare for a visit from Governor Pontius Pilate within the hour!' That was all he said: he did not ask if it was convenient; he did not even ask if Herod was home; he just made the pronouncement and turned around and left.

"When Herod heard this, he bristled. 'What does that interloper want with me?' he fumed. 'I have nothing to say to him. He sits in the palace that rightly belongs to me, and he rules Judea, which should have been mine. It was my father who built the palace he lives in, and the Temple and other grand buildings were here before he ever intruded. Now this Roman who knows nothing about us sits in the place of authority, and he sends a messenger giving orders like a man would order his slaves, and I have no choice. I must receive him and be cordial. If he is seeking a quarrel with me, I am at a disadvantage, and I do not like that.' And so he fumed, but he also worried.

"Pilate arrived at Herod's palace with a bodyguard of fifty soldiers, large, tall men with blond hair, evidently from Scandia. They were an impressive sight in their colorful uniforms. Pilate was ushered into the great hall where Herod, dressed in his finest robe, met him. Pilate seemed to be worried, even preoccupied. Without waiting for small talk, he plunged into the matter on his mind. 'It's this Jesus thing,' he said.

"At first, Herod did not comprehend. Was Pilate going to condemn him for the way he and his soldiers had mocked Jesus? Was he unhappy that he had failed to condemn him when obviously Pilate had not only condemned him, but executed him as well? Since he did not know how Pilate felt about these matters, Herod thought it would be better if he remained silent and let Pilate continue.

" 'I had no choice,' explained Pilate. 'I wanted to let him go, but I couldn't; you can understand that, can't you?'

"His tone of voice, his worried countenance — Pilate looked like a weak, beaten man. Herod relaxed; Pilate was not here to attack him or accuse him; he was here looking for sympathy, for someone to understand, for someone to listen to the anguish of his heart.

"Pilate continued: 'You know, Herod, we are alike, we both carry similar burdens. You killed John the Baptist, and I killed Jesus.' Then he laughed a nervous, hollow laugh. 'We are the exterminators!' The guilty smile fell from his face like a mask, and Herod could see that he was a frightened man. 'Tell me,' he said, 'did you have nightmares after you killed John? Did it haunt you? Did it bother you?'

"These questions touched something deep in Herod, and he was tempted to bare his soul and confess all his fears to this man who evidently felt the same things, but he held back, and simply answered, 'Yes, yes.'

"Pilate looked at him steadily, trying to read his soul, his darkest secrets through his eyes. He thought he did; 'He knows,' he said to himself. 'Do you worry about the judgment of God for your deed?' Before Herod could answer, he went on. 'In the street yesterday as I walked along, an old man in the crowd shouted out, "Pontius Pilate, you are now under the curse of God because you have murdered God's son. You will know no peace, disasters will befall you, and you will fall into the pit of Hades." Then he was gone, but his words struck terror in my soul. My wife had tried to stop me from doing this deed, and she has told me the same thing. Now I think it is true.'

" 'At least you have a wife who tried to warn you; mine pushed me into it. Now I cannot even bring up the subject or she belittles me and calls me a weakling. I think she feels guilty too, but she is hard — harder than I am.'

"Pilate said, 'I wish my wife was harder; she walks around grieving as though the world has come to an end. She tells me I ought to repent of my great evil and throw myself on the mercy of God. That I will never do! And she knows it, and then she weeps some more. I think she is largely responsible for this feeling of impending doom that sometimes comes over me like a gloomy cloud, that shuts out the sun and fills me with darkness and dread. Do you think I did wrong to condemn Jesus?'

"Herod considered his answer carefully for a while. He remembered the awful waves of guilt that swept over him when he realized what he had done to John. He remembered the fierce anger he had felt toward Herodias. He felt that she had trapped him and wanted to make her suffer as she had made him suffer. He discovered that this anger toward his wife helped to assuage his guilt, and he thought of this as he answered Pilate.

" 'Don't blame yourself,' he said. 'Blame the leaders of his people. They were the ones who wanted him dead, demanded his crucifixion. They are the guilty ones, not you.'

" 'I know this,' replied Pilate, 'and I tell myself this over and over again. I have even washed my hands again in that same basin, but the blood remains on my hands. I allowed those people to push me around and make a decision I did not want to make. Well, I won't let that happen again. I will make some decisions they won't like; I will see to it that they feel some of the anguish they have pushed on me.' Pilate stood up and paced back and forth with agitation. 'They will find out that Pilate can be firm, yes, hard — yes, harsh. We will see how they like that.'

"Herod did not like what he saw; it would not take much to push Pilate over the edge, so he sought to quiet him. 'You are a Roman, a noble Roman,' he said, putting his hand on Pilate's shoulder, 'and to a Roman, justice is everything, even-handed justice. You are here to see that Roman law is respected. Do that. Don't let this minor, unfortunate event spoil your excellent reputation.'

"Pilate stopped his pacing and sat down. 'You are right, Herod. I must think of my place in history. I will be fair, but I will no longer listen to the leaders of this nation. I will run it like a Roman province from now on, and I will disregard their religious leaders.

"Pilate got up to leave, but Herod said, 'Don't hurry away; stay a while. Let's walk in my garden and have some wine. We have much in common; we are busy men, but we deserve some enjoyment and peace once in a while.'

"Pilate relaxed with a long sigh. He had been tense so long; now he felt like a bow with its string suddenly loosed. He said, 'Herod, I like you. We speak the same language and share the same burdens. We should visit more often.' Then they went out into the garden. It was nightfall before Pilate returned to his palace.

" That night he lay on his bed and thought over his prospects. It did no good to lament deeds already done; he would focus on the future. He would no longer worry about the leaders and what they thought; he was the governor and he intended to govern. He would do what was best for the Roman empire, even if the Jews were destroyed in the process.

" 'I know what I will do,' he said to himself in a sudden inspiration. 'I will send to Rome for a building engineer, and I will begin some great project. That will take my mind off my problems, and make sure that I will be remembered in history.' It sounded like a good idea, but it ended in so much controversy that it became one giant headache for him.

"In due time, the engineer arrived from Rome, a man named Cellus, a competent man who had done some noteworthy building projects. Pilate took him on a tour through Jerusalem as a first step in determining what kind of project was suitable. When Cellus saw the Temple, he stood in awe, silent, and then murmured several times, 'Magnificent, magnificent!' He had the same reaction to some of the palaces, the theater, the arena, all built by Herod the Great. 'What is left for me to do?' asked Pilate. 'How could I ever match the greatness of all this?'

" 'Give me a day or two, and I will let you know. A city always needs something, and I will find the right monument for you.' Cellus spoke with authority, and Pilate thought to himself, 'Good man! He will help me make a name for myself.'

"A week later Cellus appeared at Pilate's door with a roll of plans under his arm. 'The city needs a more dependable water supply,' he announced. 'This has always been one of Rome's major contributions to the civilized world — the Roman aqueduct. This is what I propose for Jerusalem.' He spread out the plans and pointed to the spot two hundred furlongs from Jerusalem where water could be obtained and the route the aqueduct would take. 'It cuts right through the city, so it ought to be elaborate to blend in with the other buildings.'

"Pilate was apprehensive. 'Won't the people object to this structure coming through the city? Many homes would have to be destroyed; the cost of building would be enormous.'

"Cellus eyed Pilate closely and said, 'People always object. If you left it to the vote of the people, nothing worthwhile would ever be built. They cannot see beyond their own noses, or at least beyond their own front door. As for the cost, that which costs little, is worth little, and will not stand the test of time. I am interested in building for the ages, monuments that will be here long after I am gone. This is the way you should think. Be a builder, Pilate! Think large thoughts! Do great things!'

"Pilate was carried away with his oratory; he felt good about himself. He straightened up, threw out his chest, and proclaimed, 'Build the aqueduct, build a great aqueduct, and let it stand for all the ages to come to show that Pilate once ruled in Jerusalem.'

"Hundreds of workers were hired, and the work began. 'It is wise,' explained Cellus to Pilate, 'to begin at the far end. If we begin in Jerusalem, there will be trouble. After we have much done, it will be unstoppable. You will have your aqueduct.'

"When the work began, the grumbling began, and when the work increased, the grumbling increased. People went out to see the project and came home to speculate where the great aqueduct would enter the city and what homes would be demolished in the process. There were many conjectures and consequently many sections of the city were in tumult. The leaders were apprehensive, and their apprehension increased when the people began to put pressure on them to stop the project. The people insisted, 'This Roman intends to deface our Holy City! If we let him continue with this monstrosity, our city will be ruined forever. And what about our homes? Will Rome build us better ones? No! We will be left out in the cold.'

"The leaders did not know how to answer; they had never been consulted, never notified of the decisions. They had been completely ignored, and this put them in a bad position. One of them stood up and said, 'What we need is a leader who will stand up to this despot, someone who will speak for us and for our concerns.' The storm of anger was rising, so the High Priest rose and told them all to go home. 'We will talk to Pilate,' he said, 'We will see that this is stopped.'

"They made an urgent appointment to see Pilate and went to the Fortress of Antonia to meet him in the judgment hall. This part pleased them. They said, 'At least he understands how important this matter is. It is better here than trying to talk about this as he sits in his bath.' But Pilate had other ideas. As they stood before him, the governor began the conversation by saying. 'About the building project ...' He took a long breath, rearranged his robes, and scowled in a way that he thought must look quite regal. He was doing all this, they knew, for dramatic effect, and they wondered what was coming next.

" 'About this building project,' he continued, 'I know it does not have popular support, but I was not sent here by Tiberius to gather popular support. I was sent here to look after the interests of Rome and to do what is best for the city. One of the most important resources for a city is a dependable, adequate supply of water. We do not have that now, but I will see to it that we will soon. During your festivals, so many people crowd into the city that water becomes scarce. As a good governor, I cannot allow that to continue. But these things cost money, and those who benefit should share in the expense. I have made a generous contribution to begin this great project, but from now on, you will finance it out of your Temple tax. You certainly can afford it!'

"A murmur of protest went up, and the High Priest said excitedly, 'That we cannot do! That money belongs to God, not to us. We cannot touch that money!'

" 'You touch that money to build your own palaces and to line your pockets,' sneered Pilate. 'Don't pretend that you have no control over that money.'

" 'But it is God's money,' protested one of the priests.

" 'Then I will send the bill to your God, but I will hold you responsible for his debts. I give you permission to leave now.'

"They left filled with equal measures of confusion and anger. What could they do now? The people would not tolerate this! When they gathered to discuss their dilemma, one of them spoke these wise words: 'If we let Pilate get away with this, he will run us into the ground and take away all of our money. What is to stop him from doubling the tax to pay for his next project? And what will the people say when they hear that their sacred money is going to pay for this scheme that they hate so much? But I know what we must do. Remember when Pilate brought those accursed shields into the Temple? He did not listen when we complained, but when the people came, thousands of them, and he saw what a tumult was raised, he changed his mind. The only thing that can move Pilate is force! This is what we must do.

" 'Since Temple money is involved, this is a matter that concerns all of Israel, and all must protest this crime against our nation. Before this Passover, we must get the word to every city and town, from Dan to Beersheba, and we must take our stand. Especially tell the people of Galilee; they are always ready to take on Rome. And if we die in the attempt, then we die!'

"To this, they all agreed. I can understand that; Pilate had backed them into a corner, and their leadership and honor were at stake. When the word came to Capernaum, there was a ready response. This was a just cause, a holy war. But when Zebedee talked to me about it, I had to warn him that this kind of action could lead to trouble. 'That makes no difference,' he told me. 'This is what we must do.' Then he wanted me to promise to keep this matter a secret, and I couldn't help myself — I laughed out loud. 'Do you think Pilate does not know about this already,' I laughed. 'He has his spies and they are well-paid and well-informed. You can count on it that Pilate will be prepared for any trouble that comes. I only hope that you are not chewed up in the process.'

"I could see that this could not be stopped, and so, when they left to go to Jerusalem for the Passover, I warned them to be careful and prudent. 'I would like to see you back here again when this is over,' I told them. 'Don't do anything foolish.'

"The showdown came much as I had predicted. Pilate was prepared for the disturbance, although he was not prepared for the size of the crowd that gathered. Maxus told me that the crowd must have numbered more than twenty thousand angry, shouting people. At first it appeared that Pilate was going to take the diplomatic approach; he started to make a speech, talking about the good of the great city, about water being the most necessary thing to life. But the crowd was restless, milling about like cattle. Then one man with a loud voice shouted out, 'We don't want to hear your smooth words, you Roman monster; we want this aqueduct stopped, and we want it stopped right now.' The crowd roared its approval until the hills rang with the echo of the shouts.

"After a long, long time, Pilate was able to quiet them enough to begin to speak, but he started off on the wrong foot. He said angrily, 'I am in charge here and ...' At that, the crowd began to hoot and stamp their feet. Then one young man — they tell me he was from Galilee — broke through the crowd and threw a handful of dirt at Pilate. This startled him so much that he stumbled as he tried to avoid the small cloud of dust descending on him. Others began to join in, throwing sticks, and some even small coins. Pilate's bodyguards stepped in, and Pilate took a sword and held it over his head.

"What the crowd did not know, but were soon to learn, was that this was the signal to the soldiers who were scattered throughout the crowd and surrounding it. They were not in their military uniforms; if they had been, perhaps the crowd would have thought twice about abusing a Roman governor. From under his ordinary clothes, each man took out his sword and waded into the unarmed crowd, striking in every direction. At the first sign of the slaughter, the people panicked, running in every direction, but the soldiers were everywhere, striking at anyone in reach, men, women, and even children. The slaughter was terrible.

"I had warned the group from Capernaum to stay out of trouble, and although they did not take part in the disturbance and were on the far edge of the crowd, it made no difference to the soldiers; they were hit as they simply stood there. Elder Ezra was stabbed in the arm as he was seeking to protect his wife. Sarah was hit on the side of the head with the flat side of a sword, and many of the young men, who perhaps were not innocent bystanders, were killed. Those who could, fled; those who could not were finished off by the soldiers.

"Pilate was heard to say after it was over, 'That's the only way to handle these people. I do not expect trouble from them again. I will make my own decisions, and they will live with them.' The leaders had not heard him say this, but nobody needed to spell out this message for them. From now on, they would be ruled by an angry tyrant. Times would be hard for them."

9

For the next few days, Livy thought about what Pilate had done to the Jews in Jerusalem, and somehow it bothered him. He was a good Roman, and had originally thought of writing this history to show that Roman rule of the world was a good, unifying thing. Now he was not so sure. *Roman governors ought to symbolize the best of Roman justice,* he thought as he entered Castor's courtyard. *How can Roman rule be good if Roman rulers are evil? I will have to ask Castor about that.*

Castor was not surprised at the question; it was one he had to face time after time. Often he had to defend Rome's actions to Zebedee when he knew that there was no real defense. He had come to some conclusions for himself so that he was able to live and work in the system without agreeing to every part.

"It would take a long time to explain this, if truly it could be explained at all," began Castor, rubbing his chin and looking for all the world like a philosopher. "We live in an imperfect world, and we deal with imperfect people. It may be that no man has the wisdom and the personal skills to govern people who do not want to be governed. It always results in rule by force. The Roman Empire without the Roman army is nothing, and it would disintegrate into fragments and pieces, hundreds of tribes and nations warring among themselves and against each other. Take the Jewish nation, for example. If we withdrew the Roman army, they would declare their independence the next day, and that is what they are long-ing for and praying for. But how did they do before we came along? I'll tell you — one war after another, one occupation after another, one inva-sion after another. And when they were not being threatened by others, the north fought the south. They are better off now than they were during some of the dark days of their history. I served in my post as a friend of Israel, not as an oppressor."

"That may be true for you, but what about a man like Pilate? How can you defend actions like his?"

"I cannot defend him," said Castor. "I didn't defend him then, and I don't defend him now. But I will say this in defense of the Roman Empire; although justice for Pilate was slow and came too late for many of his victims, it came nevertheless, and he was removed. And that is what I want to tell you about today — the last days of Pontius Pilate. But let me begin at the beginning of my story.

"One day Alex and Sarah came to see me about a curious matter. Alex wanted to find the man who had saved his life when they were attacked on the Jericho road. Seeing Kish at the crucifixion had stirred his memory, and he began to realize that all the life and happiness he had enjoyed since that time had been due to the kindness of someone he had never even met and never had the opportunity to thank. The more he thought of this, the more he determined to find this man and thank him.

" 'It will help to even up the accounts of the world,' said Alex, half in jest. 'Every act of kindness ought to be balanced by a gift of thanksgiving. Look at this.' He then pulled a beautiful silver signet ring out of his purse. It was a masterful work! 'This is what I have made for my benefactor, and I would like to give it to him personally.'

"You see, Livy, there were problems with this well-intentioned plan. First of all, the benefactor was a Samaritan, and traditionally, the Jews have nothing to do with the Samaritans. But Alex was a Greek, so this didn't matter so much to him, but still Capernaum was like a small town, and the neighbors would have strong feelings about this. For that reason, Sarah thought she could not consider going with him.

"But there was also another problem, and the problem was Pilate. His actions were becoming more violent, more unreasonable, and the Samaritans were now feeling the cutting edge of Pilate's rage. 'Is it safe for him to go there?' Sarah asked me.

"I had to reply to her, 'No place is completely safe, but he should avoid the center of any disturbance. That way he will survive, unless some major catastrophe occurs.' Then I turned to Alex and said, 'But how do you intend to find him? All you know is that his name is Seema.'

" 'I also know that he is a merchant, and evidently a successful one, since he did business over such a wide area. Someone is sure to know him!'

"We had some more discussion, but it was evident that Alex felt that this was something he had to do in order to repay such a magnanimous act of kindness. The next day he left to begin his search, and here is the story he told us when he returned."

✳ ✳ ✳ ✳ ✳ ✳

"I decided I would begin my search in the city of Sakaria — no particular reason — I had to begin somewhere. When I arrived in the city, I sensed that something was wrong, something felt strange. At first I could not put my finger on it, but then I began to notice things. There were very few people around; most of the shops were closed. Then it dawned on me; I had seen no men, only women and children. I was about to approach a small group of women to ask why but when they saw me approaching, they discreetly moved away. Of course! I was dressed like a Jew and looked like a Jew!

"On my way there I had decided that the best place to begin would be the inn; most innkeepers know who comes and who goes. I was not surprised to find the inn empty; the people who had a day's journey to make were already on their way. By the time I found the innkeeper, I was filled with curiosity, and I suppose, a little bit of apprehension. This was strange indeed!

"I found the innkeeper at the back gate, dragging in bags of grain. He was a large man — not a tall man, but a large man. The belt around his waist would go around mine twice with some to spare. His arms were like tree trunks, and his legs were like the pillars of the Temple, except that they were bowed, perhaps to fit more comfortably around the sides of a fat donkey — a large, fat donkey, the only kind that could easily carry such a man. His head was large and round and appeared even larger because of his bushy hair and beard. He tossed the grain sacks around as though they were nothing, and I thought, *I would not like to meet this fellow on a deserted road on a dark night*. At least, I thought that until he turned around, and when I saw his open, friendly face, I liked him instantly, and I was sure that I would be safe with him anywhere.

"He straightened up and wiped his brow with the back of his hand and said, 'Are you looking for lodging?' Hesitantly, I said, 'No.' I was not sure at that point where I would be going. Before I could explain, he said, 'Then how about something to eat? My wife makes the best barley lamb stew you ever ate.' Now I could see why he was so round and firm, and I decided that with such an advertisement for his wife's cooking, I could not go wrong, and I could probably learn more over a plate of stew than talking in the yard, so I accepted the invitation.

"He was right about the stew, and I was right that I could learn what I wanted to know over a friendly meal. 'What is going on here?' I asked after we had begun to eat. I did not need to explain my question; he knew. However, his answer completely puzzled me: 'It's this Gerizim matter.' When he saw that I did not know what he was talking about, he went on to tell me a strange story.

"Pilate's treatment of the Samaritans had become unbearable. Leaders had been taken captive and killed without just reason. Lands had been confiscated, and now he seemed determined to wipe out the religion that was the center of Samaritan life. They had sent leaders to Caesarea to reason with him, but the leaders had never returned. Consequently, rumors had spread that they, also, had been killed. A great gloom had settled over all the people, and a great fear as well.

"Then one day a man named Essar came from the hills and began to proclaim the only message of hope that they had heard for a long time. He said that Moses had hidden sacred vessels from the Tabernacle in the Wilderness in a secret place on Mount Gerizim, and that these sacred objects would protect them from any evil.

"At this point I interrupted him and said, 'But Moses never crossed the Jordan; he never got as far as Gerizim.'

" 'That's what everyone thinks,' he replied, 'but Essar says that is not true, and he is prepared to prove it. The people want to believe this, not only for the divine protection the vessels will give them, but also to prove that Mount Gerizim is God's mountain — not Jerusalem.'

" 'So where are all the people?' I asked him.

" 'They have gathered at a town named Tirath, to the north of here. Essar is preparing to lead them to the sacred vessels, so nearly all of the men of our town have gone to join the procession.'

"I thought about this for a moment and then asked, 'Why aren't you with them?'

" 'Well, first,' he explained, 'I don't believe what Essar says; I think it will be a big disappointment to them all. Also, the travelers who depend on my service will want to be fed and cared for; I have a good business to run, and that comes first with me.'

"Then I asked him the question that had brought me there: 'Do you know a merchant named Seema?'

"When he hesitated, I knew that my search was going to be a long one. Then he said, 'I think I might know him, but he never stayed with me. Most likely he lives in a neighboring town. I know he does not live in Sakaria, because I know everybody in town, and in the next town, too.'

"As I began to think of my options, he said to me, 'Since so many people from all over are gathered in Tirath, why don't you go there and ask? That's your best chance.' So I started on the road to Tirath.

"I approached the town from the south, and I was to learn later that this was fortunate. I found the town nearly as empty as Sakaria, and the few men who remained were making their way out of town to the north. I followed these stragglers, and outside of town in a field, I found the attraction that was drawing the manhood of the Samaritans like a magnet. On a tree stump stood this man Essar, holding forth and gesticulating wildly. When I saw him, I thought, *'All these self-styled prophets look alike.* His hair was wild; I am sure no comb had touched it for years; in fact, it was so wild, so exaggerated, that I think he must have worked on it to achieve that effect. His robe appeared to be a collection of grain sacks, and for a belt he used a rope that had, no doubt, been used to lead a donkey until it became too worn and frayed to be dependable.

"I was too far away to hear what he was saying, and I never got any closer. Essar lifted his fist toward heaven and let out a shout that was answered by every man in the crowd until before me I saw a sea of waving fists and heard shouts which rang to the heavens. Then, like the waves of the sea, the crowd began to move, pushing and shoving, funneling down the road that led north to Mount Gerizim.

"It was here that I remembered Castor's advice, to stay out of the way of trouble, but I could not resist the temptation to follow along to see what would come of this project that the innkeeper thought was some kind of hoax. If it was a hoax, no one will ever know; Essar and his pilgrimage never reached the mount, never had a chance to prove the truth — or more likely — the falsehood that inspired such a crowd to follow after him.

"They never reached the mount because their way was barred by Pilate's army led by the cavalry. No, I shouldn't say barred — that perhaps could be forgiven — it was much worse. Pilate's spies had informed him of the gathering mob and in his warped mind, he concluded that they were going to march to overthrow and kill him. If he had heard about the sacred vessels, he didn't believe a bit of it, and he had deemed that it would be necessary to stamp out this rebellion as he had done in Jerusalem. So, without discussion, without warning, he gave the order for the cavalry to charge into the mass of humanity before them.

"A cry went up that I will never forget, a cry of terror, the screams of the wounded and the dying. I did not wait to see if they would reach me; I beat a hasty retreat. From a sheltered spot on the hills above, I could see what was happening. When the men began to flee, the army began to drive them back into town, and they encircled hundreds of them, including Essar. *What will they do with this crowd?* I wondered. After a little while, their purpose became clear. Evidently the captain had gone to Pilate for orders, and without hesitation the order was given: "Kill them all!" This was even worse, to see the defenseless men slaughtered like animals.

"I had seen enough, too much! I wish I had left before the bloodshed. If I had known what was going to happen, I would not have gone near the place.

"I gave up my search for Seema. My chances of finding him had disappeared, and my heart was overcome with grief because of what I had seen. That was enough! I came home."

✳ ✳ ✳ ✳ ✳ ✳

Castor watched Livy writing his notes on his wax tablets, frowning as he did so. "This is just the sort of thing I did not want to hear," he said sadly. "How will this sound in a history that is supposed to favor Roman rule?"

Castor replied, "That part will not sound good, but you cannot omit it or the rest of the story will not fit. You will like this part better. Of course, at that time we did not know this part, and the embarrassment that I felt certainly exceeded yours, because I was wearing the uniform of Rome. But eventually, Rome did not fail them. Later we learned the outcome of that incident.

"Shortly after a period of deep mourning, what was left of the Samaritan senate met to discuss their dilemma and concluded that unless they appealed this injustice and got some Roman relief, they would be completely destroyed. Consequently, they sent a delegation to Vitellius, legate to Syria, the highest Roman official in that part of the world. Vitellius listened silently, but they could see the anger rising in his cheeks; this was a shame to Rome, an affront to Roman justice.

"At first, the Samaritans did not know whether the anger they saw in his face would be directed at them or at Pilate. They did not have to wait long to find out. 'Pilate is out!' he said with force and finality. 'I will give the order at once, before this day is out. Pilate is no longer governor. I will order him to appear before Caesar to answer for his crimes, and I, myself, will prepare the papers against him.'

"That was the end of Pilate's reign of terror. His wife Procula felt relieved in a way, but new fears engulfed her. Was this the time that God would visit judgment on Pilate for the evil he had done? Would God use Rome as His instrument? Caesar Tiberius would show no mercy. What would happen to Pilate? They began their long journey to Rome, never to return to Israel. However, before they arrived in Rome, Caesar Tiberius died.

"Now let me jump ahead in my story to finish this part about Pilate. The new Emperor, Caligula, had too many things on his mind to give much attention to the crimes of Pilate, so he simply banished him in disgrace, and sent him far to the north. Pilate decided he could find solace and peace at the beautiful lake called Lucerne, and since he was a wealthy man, he could have expected to finish his days in peace and contentment. I know this would not seem fair to you, Livy, with your sense of historic justice. You will be relieved to know it did not happen that way.

"Pilate brought his own judgment and condemnation with him. His guilty conscience gave him no rest. Procula watched her husband suffer, and it pained her greatly. Again and again she tried to talk to him about it. 'God is a God of mercy and forgiveness," she told him. Pilate would reply, 'There is no mercy for me; look at my hands! Can you see the blood? All the waters of Lucerne cannot wash away these stains.' Procula replied tenderly but firmly, 'On the cross, Jesus himself prayed, "Father, forgive them, for they know not what they do." There is forgiveness for you if you will seek it.'

" 'No,' replied Pilate, 'there is none for me. I knew what I was doing. You know that! You yourself warned me about it, and I am sure that all of your prophecy will come to pass, and nothing can stop it.'

"And so the conversation would end, every time. Pilate could not sleep, could not eat. He grew worn and haggard. One day he went down to the lake and stood on a high cliff. As he looked at the waters far below, he thought it was the pit of Hades and he felt some irresistible force pulling him downward. He could resist no longer. With a long, drawn-out scream, he plunged headfirst into the abyss. His body was not recovered until several days later."

10

Two weeks had passed before Livy made his next appointment with Castor, and during that time, he had been busy writing and rewriting his material. In his mind, he concluded that this place in Rome's history would be a good place to begin the next section; a new section, a new emperor, a new beginning. He mentioned this to Castor and was surprised when he said that the new beginning would have to wait.

"We are not ready for that yet," said Castor. "There is another strand that we must pick up and weave into this historical tapestry. I think you will see that the picture is incomplete without this one. The death of Tiberius is a turning point in this story too, but we have to back up a bit and approach it from another direction."

"I can see what you mean about the twisted strands of history; no one story stands by itself, and one cannot understand the present without first understanding the past. Who do we talk about this time?"

"Another Herod — Herod Agrippa," said Castor.

"Another Herod? I was hoping we would be through with them. They have been a blot on my manuscript. Where does he fit in?"

Castor scratched his head as though he was trying to stimulate his thinking, without success, so he said, "The Herod family is so convoluted that I cannot keep them all straight no matter how hard I try. To begin with, Herod the Great had so many wives and children, so many with the same names, and so many intermarrying that it becomes a hopeless task. The Herod we are talking about now was one of the grandsons of Herod the Great and the brother of Herodias who was married to Herod Philip before she left him to go with Herod Antipas."

"Wait a minute!" said Livy who was trying to write it all down. "Go over that again; I can't figure it out at all."

"Don't let that bother you," said Castor with a chuckle. "Let me tell you about this fellow and what he did; his complicated genealogy is not my point here.

"I saw him first in Tiberias. I had gone there on the emperor's business

75

and was staying with my friend Justin. As we walked down the street toward the palace, Justin stopped in the middle of a conversation and said, 'Look — see that man there? He is the new magistrate of this city.'

" 'What?' I said. 'Why do you need a magistrate as long as Kooza is in charge here?'

" 'That's just the point; we don't,' laughed Justin. 'It is a position that has no meaning and was created just to make him feel good.'

" 'Now that is a curious situation,' I said. 'How did this come about? Who is that man?'

" 'That man is Herod Agrippa,' said Justin, 'and I feel obliged to tell you that man's very unflattering story. Here, let's sit in the shade on this bench and I will give you a little history lesson about our new magistrate.'

"Since I have always been interested in history, I was happy to listen. What I did not know then was that this man would bring sorrow to my good friend Zebedee, and consequently to me. That man would order the unjust murder of James. Now here is the story he told me."

* * * * * *

"I think you know, Castor, that the Herods consider themselves Jews, but the Jews say this is only partly true. What bothers them most is that they act and think like Romans, not Jews. Now take this man Agrippa, for example. He was brought up in Rome, not Jerusalem— and not even in the Jewish community in Rome. His best friend was the son of Tiberius, Drew. His mother, Bernice, who was a most remarkable woman, was a close friend of Caesar, and like any mother, had ambitions for her son. Agrippa was in a good position to succeed.

"Agrippa was a friendly fellow with one glaring fault — he couldn't hang on to his money. This flaw was magnified by an insecurity that made him feel that he had to give gifts — rich gifts to people to be liked by them — and he carried this to the extreme. His friends called him generous and even magnanimous, but in reality, he was a spendthrift, trying to buy the friendship of anyone who could help him socially or politically. His mother was alarmed at the way he went through money. She often lectured him about this, and even kept him on a limited allowance. This worked quite well as long as she was alive, but when she died, with no one to hold him back, he began to spend money at such a rate and give such lavish gifts that he soon went through the family fortune, and then began to borrow money from anyone who was foolish enough to lend to him. He was not the first to live far beyond his means, and I am sure he will not be the last. He lived on such a grand scale that his debts became mountainous. He still owes Caesar's treasury three hundred thousand pieces of silver, and he has nothing!"

✳ ✳ ✳ ✳ ✳ ✳

"Justin stopped his conversation to direct my attention to three women who were walking a short distance from us and said to me, 'There — that middle woman — that's Agrippa's wife. Her name is Cypros. I really admire her; any other woman would have left him long ago and gone back to mother. If she had not stuck by him, he would be dead today!'

"I lifted my eyebrows slightly to indicate that I thought that this was perhaps an exaggeration, but he hurried on to assure me that he meant what he said, and meant that literally. And this is what he told me.

✳ ✳ ✳ ✳ ✳ ✳

"She really did save his life. When the money ran out, Agrippa saw that they could no longer stay in Rome. By this time, Sejanus had killed his friend Drew because he was in line for the throne, and Tiberius was so heartbroken that he would not see any of Drew's friends because they reawakened his grief. Agrippa felt that his life had come to an end; his money was gone and he was deeply in debt; his influential friend was dead, and Caesar would not even allow his name to be mentioned in his presence. Now, since his creditors saw that he was without royal support, they began to hound him unmercifully. So he fled from Rome and went to hide in a tower in Idumea near the Arabian desert. This only intensified his depression, and he talked of taking his own life. He would have, too, but every method of suicide entailed some pain, and he didn't have the courage to go through with it.

"Cypros did her best to shake him out of his deep depression, but she saw that things would only get worse if they stayed where they were. The little money they had managed to borrow was running out, and she was sure that when that was gone, Agrippa would kill himself. Cypros said to herself, 'I have no choice but to appeal to his sister, Herodias, for help.' She could not talk to Agrippa about this, because he was not on best terms with his sister, but Cypros could see no other way to survive. So she wrote the letter, and in time, got a favorable reply. She went to

Agrippa, excited and happy, and said to him, 'Look, Agrippa, your sister and Herod want us to come and live in Tiberias. Isn't that good news?'

" 'No! I won't go and take charity from them. They would look down on me as a poor relative, and laugh behind my back. No! I will die first,' Then he stormed out, more depressed than ever. He climbed to the top of the tower and looked at the rocks below, but the height frightened him, and he was afraid to climb up on the parapet.

"Cypros did not give up; she wrote an urgent letter suggesting that the only way to save Agrippa was to save his pride. 'He needs to feel that he is important' she wrote. 'I beg of you, create some job with a high-sounding title for him, even if it is meaningless; otherwise, I am sure that he will take his life soon.'

"When Herodias talked to Herod about this, he said, 'Let him take his life! He is a fool! The world would be better off without him!' But Herodias kept at it, and finally Herod relented and wrote an official letter asking Agrippa to come and be magistrate of Tiberias.

"When he arrived here, Herod said, 'See, he is a fool. He doesn't even realize that the job is meaningless. He would starve to death without my help, and if it wasn't for his wife, I would let him starve.'

" 'And you stay away from her, or you will have to answer to me about it!' said Herodias, her eyes blazing with warning. She was willing to put forth some effort to save her brother, but she was not willing to put up with another affair by her husband."

******

"I did not see Justin for quite a while, but the next time we met, I was anxious to hear of the progress the new 'magistrate.' 'Oh, he is gone,' said Justin. 'You should have been here! What a battle!'

" 'Tell me about it,' I said. So Justin told me this.

******

"They were having one of their many banquets, and the wine was flowing freely. Both Herod and Agrippa had problems with wine; both became unpredictable, even belligerent when they had too much. This night, after they had consumed quite a bit, they began to call to each other; it began in jest, and some humorous things were said. The guests laughed, I think much more than the humor warranted, but after all,

Herod was the governor and they were eating his food.

"After a while, the jesting became more pointed, and then cruel. Herod was getting the better of Agrippa and then belittled his manhood, and when the room rocked with laughter, Agrippa turned red with embarrassment, but also rage. In a fit of anger, he insulted Herod and then their exchanges became vicious. Agrippa lost his temper completely and threw a plate of food at Herod. When it splattered all over his fancy robe, Herod lost control. 'You miserable worm!' he shouted, trembling with rage, eyes bulging, the veins in his neck standing out. 'You miserable worm! I have taken you in and fed you to keep you from starving, and this is your thanks! If your wife hadn't begged me to take you, you would have starved in that tower, or better yet, you would have had the good sense to jump off headfirst and smash your few, feeble brains on the rocks below. Now, get out of my sight, you sponge; go live off of someone else for a while. It is obvious that you cannot make an honest living for yourself, but you will get no more from me. I don't care if you starve.'

"This tirade devastated Agrippa. He was hurt by the humiliation in front of others, and Herod had robbed him of his last shred of self-confidence. He had thought he was earning his way, but all of that collapsed in a moment, and he was left with nothing — no self-respect, no place to live, no way to support himself, no hope for the future. Even hard-hearted Herodias felt sorry for him, and later that night, she went to see him. She found them packing their possessions, getting ready to move. 'Don't be so hasty,' she said. 'I'll speak to Herod tomorrow when he feels better; perhaps he will change his mind.'

" 'No! Don't do me any more favors,' he replied in anger. 'I would rather starve in the desert than stay here one more day. We will be gone before the sun rises.'

" 'Then, here, take this,' said Herodias, and she handed him a bag of silver coins.

"In anger, he threw the bag across the room, shouting as he did it, 'I don't need your help; I don't need help from anyone. Leave us alone!'

"Herodias left, knowing that she could be of no more help to her brother. The first thing Agrippa did when the door closed was to pick up the bag and count the coins. Cypros said nothing; she knew better than to talk to him when he was in that kind of mood. As I said before, most women would have left him, but she did not. When they left Tiberius as the first rays of the sun came up over the lake, she was at his side. They went north. We may never see them again. Poor Cypros!"

✳ ✳ ✳ ✳ ✳ ✳

Livy looked up from his notes with a smile and said, "That was not the last you heard of them, was it?"

"No," said Castor, "it wasn't, but for a long time we didn't know where they went or what happened to them. However, the network of centurions covers the world, and little by little, in bits and pieces, I learned the story from the centurions who crossed his path. This man, who was to become king of the Jews, became a fugitive, on the wrong side of the law, and all because of money. The theme kept repeating, over and over again, and he never seemed to learn from his past mistakes. A person who is always in debt is always in trouble, and that can ruin all of life. Take a lesson from this, Livy; do not spend what you do not have. Living on borrowed money is the road to sorrow, and I know of no better example than Agrippa. When you write this part of your history, you would do well to do a little preaching. Someone might listen to your advice and avoid some real heartache. But back to the story.

" 'Where are we going?' asked Cypros when they were on the road. 'What do we do now?'

"Agrippa had cooled down and the emotional explosion of the past night had left him quiet and moody. Reality was beginning to confront him, and he was thinking of ways to solve his immediate, pressing problem. 'Flaccus is our answer,' he said after walking a while in silence. I need to tell you, Livy, that Flaccus was a noble Roman, and he had been a friend of Agrippa in Rome. Now he lived in Syria and held an important post in the Roman government as consul. I have met him twice, and he is the kind of man you should write about if you want to extol the virtues of the Roman empire. He had a large estate, so when Agrippa and Cypros appeared at his door, he welcomed them and installed them in a luxurious apartment in his home and made arrangements to provide for all their needs.

"Now you might ask, 'How does this fellow always seem to fall into such advantageous circumstances? He never seems to suffer from his mistakes.' I will answer you that he carries the seeds of his own destruction within himself, and it will not be long before they will flower.

"In a few days, his discontent began to show, for two reasons. First, his brother, Aristo, was also living with Flaccus, and the two had been enemies since they were young. Often it seemed that Flaccus was sure to be caught in their arguments and bitterness, but by skillful maneuvering, he remained outside the conflict. But Agrippa began to look for ways to discredit Aristo and get him to leave.

"His second problem was money. True, Flaccus took care of all of his needs and was generous, but generous was not enough for him. Agrippa needed money, money, and more money, and he saw that he would never get it here unless he could devise some unusual scheme. He didn't have to go looking for temptation, however; it came looking for him, and it happened this way.

"There was a border dispute between Damascus and Sidon, and delegations from each came to Flaccus for a resolution of the problem. It was a complicated situation, and both had a great deal to lose by an unfavorable decision. Each side began to look for ways to strengthen their case.

"One evening, the ambassador from Damascus appeared at Agrippa's door and asked, almost in a whisper, 'Could we go for a walk in your garden?' Agrippa's eyes lit up, and his pulse beat faster. He could see what was coming. The ambassador wasted no words: I see you have influence with Flaccus. If you could help, I will see to it that you will be a rich man.'

"Agrippa had what he wanted, but he also had something he did not want, and knew nothing about. His brother had seen the ambassador making his way to Agrippa's house and said to himself, 'Now that is strange! What business could he possibly have with my brother? I had better keep an eye on this!' He did keep an eye on it, and an ear also; he heard the whole conversation.

"The next morning at breakfast, Agrippa sat near Flaccus and skillfully turned the conversation to the dispute between Damascus and Sidon. 'This is a complicated matter,' Agrippa said. 'It will take the wisdom of Solomon to resolve it properly.' To this, Flaccus agreed, and confessed that he did not know what he would do about it.' Well, it so happens,' began Agrippa, 'I have some background in these matters — clearly Damascus should prevail — but you do what is right.' Flaccus thanked him for his help, and Agrippa went on his way thinking he would be rich before the week was out, and even began to make plans in his mind to make use of his newfound wealth.

"But then Aristo went to see Flaccus! When he told his story, Flaccus called the centurion and ordered him to bring both Agrippa and the ambassador immediately for a hearing. When the centurion came for Agrippa, he knew at once why, and on the way, he tried to come up with some excuse or some explanation that would get him out of his tight spot, but he could find none. Caught off guard that way, in a few moments, the whole truth came out, and Flaccus was angry. 'Is this the way you treat my friendship?' he asked. 'Is this the way you value Roman justice? You are a disgrace to the empire. Our friendship is now at an end, and I withdraw my hospitality.'

"He was out again! As Justin said, 'Poor Cypros!'

" 'Where do we go now?' asked Cypros. How many times had she asked that? Agrippa replied, 'The only way I can advance my career is to get some help from Caesar. No one else is wise enough to see my potential; no one else has the authority to do anything worthwhile for me. We are going to Rome.'

"Perhaps that was his best opportunity, but there was one big obstacle: they had no money. When they arrived at Ptolemaïs, poverty stared them in the face. 'Who do we know here who will lend us some money?' he asked Cypros. She thought for a while and then said, 'There is one person — Peter who was your mother's steward. Perhaps he will help.' 'Yes!' replied Agrippa with enthusiasm, as though his whole life revived. 'That's the answer!'

"At once, he went to see Peter, and greeted him warmly, but Peter did not return the greeting. Before Agrippa had said a word, Peter knew what he wanted. When Bernice was alive, he had borne the brunt of Agrippa's wrath when money was not forthcoming. 'Old friend,' said Agrippa, 'I come to you in a time of great need. If you do not help me, I don't know what I will do. I need enough money to get to Rome and keep alive for a year. After that, I will be able to repay you, repay you double for your help. I promise it.'

"Peter was not impressed. 'You have defrauded me before, and have never paid back any of the loans I have made to you over the years. No. I have no money for you.'

"Agrippa saw his last hope slipping away. He was trapped, desperate. Now he could do nothing but beg, plead. 'For the memory of my mother, for the kindness she showed you, for compassion for my wife and children — Peter, Peter, give me at least something!'

"Peter was moved; he could not turn him away empty. 'I will give you the money I have with me in the house. This is all I can give.' Agrippa took it and was truly thankful and made promises that Peter knew he would never keep. He left, still professing his undying thanks.

"On the way back to Cypros, the money began to look smaller and smaller to him. 'This will not get us anywhere near Rome,' he said out loud. 'What good is this? I must use it to get to some place where a friend will lend me some substantial money.' He began searching his mind for the name of a friend with money, but one he had not cheated before. It was not an easy task. Then a name came to him; 'Alexander!' he said with a sense of discovery, even victory. 'Alexander of Alexandria. Yes, that's it! We have money enough to get there, and he will have to help us! We are going to Alexandria!'

" 'Our problems are solved,' he shouted as he approached Cypros. She listened to what he had to say, and it sounded like a good idea. Alexander was a good friend and a leader of the Jewish community in Alexandria. He was a man of compassion and wisdom. He could be a pillar of stability for her in the midst of the sinking sand that her life had become. 'Yes,' she said, 'let us go to Alexandria.' For the first time in years, she felt that there might be an answer to the chaos of their lives. They went and immediately engaged a ship that would take them to Alexandria the next day.

"While they were enjoying this feeling of euphoria, a centurion with a band of men came down the wharf. At first Agrippa did not pay any attention to them; surely they were not looking for him; he had broken no laws. But the centurion was looking for him, and after the formalities, he said, 'Our governor, Capto, has an order from Rome to apprehend you, and hold you for the debt you owe Caesar's treasury. You are ordered to pay the three hundred thousand pieces of silver, or we will have to take you into custody.' Three hundred thousand pieces of silver! Impossible! He saw all of his plans collapsing before his eyes. The little money he had would mean nothing against such a huge debt, and no one in that area could help him with such a sum. His mind worked feverishly.

" 'Come tomorrow at this time,' he said to the centurion. 'I will be prepared to pay then.'

"The centurion seemed satisfied and left to report back to the governor. 'Where are you going to get all of that money by tomorrow?' asked Cypros with deep concern. 'What are we going to do now?'

"'Don't worry,' said Agrippa, as though there was no problem at all. 'Don't worry about it; leave it to me.'

"In the middle of the night, Agrippa and his company boarded the ship, cut the ropes that secured them to the wharf, and silently sailed out into the darkness. They were gone."

11

"So they went to Alexandria!" said Livy. "Have you ever been there?"

"No," said Castor, "I haven't, but I would like to see that city before I die. I have wanted to go to Egypt ever since I was a young rookie in the army. My first captain, a man who was like a father to me, was with Julius Caesar during the Egyptian campaign, and he talked about the wonders of Egypt in glowing terms. I had hoped that I would be assigned there, especially to Alexandria, and when my orders came to go to Galilee, it was a disappointment to me; Capernaum is a far cry from Alexandria. After Rome, it is the largest city in the world, and in culture and learning, it is second to none. And the library — everyone knows it is the greatest in the world. What a time you would have there, Livy! You should really think about spending a year or two there; it would be a lifelong investment in your education. A person who has lived in both Rome and Alexandria has lived in the best the world has to offer.

"In the evenings, we would get our captain talking about his experiences there. He was happy to do so, and we were anxious to listen. I remember clearly his description of his journey there and his first sight of the shore. They had encountered several storms on the way, and most of the soldiers had had no experience on the Great Sea, and at that point had no desire to see it again. It was just before the early light of dawn when they sighted a beacon in the distance. It was the lighthouse of Alexandria. What a welcome sight! When it grew lighter, they found that the shore was not as near as they thought; the lighthouse was so large that it could be seen far out in the sea. The closer they got, the more amazed they were. What they were seeing, of course, was the lighthouse of Pharos, one of the Seven Wonders of the World. It has been standing there for three centuries. It was the first and most famous lighthouse in the world. When they got nearer, they saw a white stone tower built on a massive foundation, and our captain calculated that it was fifty times as high as a house. There was a huge iron bucket at the top, and in it, they would burn resinous wood all night; with an ingenious array of reflectors, the fire could be seen thirty-five miles out in the sea.

"Alexandria is on the western edge of the Nile delta, and if you journey south, you will come to Khufu's City of the Dead which is dominated by the Great Pyramid, another of the Seven Wonders of the World. It is so large that it defies description. Herodotus said that it took one hundred thousand men over twenty years to build. Two other pyramids are there, as well as the Sphinx. When our captain arrived there, the desert sands had covered the bottom of the figure, so Julius Caesar put part of his army to work clearing away the sand. The nose of the Sphinx is longer than a man, and it is eighty paces long. There are many monuments and tombs along the Nile, and the captain gave us a good description of many of them. Of course, they were not there on a sightseeing trip. Egypt provides a great deal of the grain that is so necessary for the empire, but to be truthful about it, the Egyptians do not supply it willingly because the empire pays very little for it. They claim that they are being impoverished, and perhaps that is true. I am sure that the grain was the reason Julius Caesar undertook the invasion."

Livy said, "I remember reading about that campaign in history. I wonder if I should include some chapters about it, and about Cleopatra, and perhaps even tracing its history back to Alexander the Great. I could write some interesting chapters."

"Yes, I'm sure you could," said Castor, "but remember we are on a detour here. We are not talking about Rome and Egypt, but rather about Rome and Israel. I would say that you ought to forget about Julius Caesar and keep your focus on Agrippa, or you will never finish your account.

"Agrippa and his party sailed into the fine harbor, one of the best in the world, and entered the city. They were surrounded by the hustle and bustle of activity. The docks were crowded with merchandise coming and going to all parts of the world. The shops and stalls that lined the streets were filled with goods and customers, and the sound of bargaining and bartering could be heard on every side. But Agrippa and Cypros were not interested in this now. Their first task was to locate Alexander, and besides, although they were dressed royally, their pockets were empty. If they were not successful in finding Alexander soon, they would be in trouble.

"Fortunately, finding Alexander was an easy task. There was a large Jewish community in the city, and it was not long before they were ushered into the airy, spacious home of the man they sought.

"Alexander was surprised to see them, and this surprise, added to the delight of the reunion, made this an exhilarating time for the weary travelers. Alexander knew that this was not a social visit; he had been well acquainted with Agrippa and his propensity to spend money. Often, while he was in Rome, Agrippa's mother sought his advice, and it was he who had advised her to dole out the money she gave him. He also was well acquainted with Cypros, and the two of them often talked at length about her place with Agrippa. Being a conservative Jewish leader, he encouraged her to persevere with him, and trust God to see some favorable conclusion.

"Alexander was a tall man, thin and angular, dressed all in black. His face was deeply lined, but the lines were character lines, not lines of worry. He was a scholar, the leading scholar and authority on the Septuagint, the Greek translation of the Hebrew Scriptures. You see, since Alexandria had been founded by Greeks, Greek was the language of the city, and in time, many of the Jews living there did not read Hebrew. It was King Ptolemy the Second who commissioned seventy scholars to make the translation. Although Hebrew is still the language of their official Scriptures, now it may be that more people read the Greek text because Greek is the language of the intellectual community.

"After the greetings, Alexander had some food brought in, and when he said the blessing for the food, he added a fervent prayer for his visitors. As he spoke in reverent tones, something stirred deep within Cypros; he seemed to be speaking directly to God, and she knew well that their only real help would come from God. When the prayer was over, Agrippa said, 'Let me tell you what brings us here.'

"Alexander raised his hand and said, 'It is too soon for that now. You are weary from your journey, and decisions made by weary people are often bad decisions. It is easier to follow a path when the sun is shining, and you are walking in the midnight gloom; I can see it in your eyes.' To that, Cypros responded with an 'Amen' that came from the depths of her soul. Alexander continued, 'When the clouds have rolled away and the sun begins to shine, we will talk and we will pray, and God will lead in the right path.'

"Later that day, Cypros said to Agrippa, 'You know, Agrippa, he speaks words of wisdom. We should listen carefully to what he says.'

"Agrippa was impatient, and unsure. 'He is a good man, I am sure, but he is also old, and I don't think he understands the pressures of the real world. I need money more than I need advice. I can make my own decisions; I just don't have the money to do what I want to do. Money is the key to everything.'

"As he was speaking, Cypros's heart was sinking. 'O Lord,' she prayed to herself, 'open his eyes and soften his heart. Keep him from destroying himself...and me.'

"Alexander could see how impatient Agrippa was; he had hoped that some time and reflection would help to give him some perspective on his life. Cypros had given him a brief account of the troubles that had brought them to that point. She had given the account without comment, making no judgment, but Alexander could understand the pressure and torment this kind of life had brought her.

"The following evening, when it became obvious that further delay would only heighten the tension, Alexander called them into his library for the consultation. Cypros was praying that something positive would emerge from the meeting; Agrippa was determined to press for some money so he could get on the road again; the inactivity was beginning to unnerve him.

"Alexander was a wise man and was skilled in dealing with difficult people, and he realized it would take a great deal of tact on his part to accomplish anything, so he began slowly. He picked up a quill pen from the ornate table beside him, held it up, looking at it for a moment, and then said, 'Agrippa, if this pen were a magic wand, and I could wave it over you and grant you one wish, what would you desire?' Without hesitation, Agrippa blurted out, 'Money!'

"Although Alexander expected this reply, he was disappointed. He did not let his disappointment show, however, but smiled and said in a kind voice, 'A hasty and ill-conceived idea! Suppose I granted that wish, but along with the money, came a painful disease that left you a cripple, unable to stir out of your bed, unable to enjoy a moment without pain — would you still ask for the same?'

"The answer was so obvious that Agrippa did not bother to reply, but deep inside, he said to himself, 'He is a wise one, all right! He is getting ready to tell me that money is not important, and then he will tell me that he won't give me any, and that will be for my own good!' He thought that, but he said nothing.

"Alexander continued, 'Money by itself is useless — any miserable miser can tell you that. It is what money can buy that gives it any value, but the things that are bought with money are not worth as much as the things that cannot be bought, the real things, the true things.' At this point, Agrippa turned off his attention; he appeared to be listening, even attentive, but he heard nothing. He was hoping that the lecture about true riches would be followed by something more substantial. He was brought back to reality when Alexander looked him in the eye and said, 'Surely the thing that drives you on is political ambition; you want power and authority more than anything else, and you see money as a means to that end. Is that not true?'

"Agrippa was surprised by this perception, and did not know how to answer. He loved money for what it could get him, but deep within was a burning ambition that he hardly admitted to himself. If he could have anything he wished with a wave of that wand, what would he choose? What did he really want?

"Alexander sensed his hesitation and almost read his thoughts. Then he said, 'Agrippa, you are like a rudderless ship, blown this way and that, first here, then there, with no compass and no anchor. You need to set a goal for your life, and establish a plan to reach it. Then you need the wisdom to see what advances you toward that goal and what hinders your progress, and the courage to choose that which advances you, choose it every time, without exception, without hesitation. Now, tell me, what is your goal?'

"Agrippa started to speak, but then stopped. Could it be that he had never figured out his true goal? Perhaps it was so. He had always been looking for advantages along the way, and he took what he could get, but now he had nothing, and he was nothing. Deep within, he had a secret that he had communicated to no one because he knew he would be ridiculed. But Alexander wanted an answer, and he would give him one! 'I want to be king of the Jews!' he said, and then wished he could pluck those words out of the air and hide them in some secret place. Surely Alexander would laugh at him, or certainly say, 'You do not have the character or spiritual power to be king of anything.' But he said nothing. He simply waited, and Agrippa thought he was obliged to give a further explanation for his brash statement.

" 'It was my grandfather who built the kingdom, rebuilt Jerusalem, built the Temple. As long as I can remember, I have taken pride in his accomplishments, and even when others spoke evil of him, I looked on him as my hero. He climbed to the top in spite of much opposition, and he built a kingdom. When he divided it into three parts. It was as though he had taken an expensive, beautiful plate and dropped it to the floor, breaking it into pieces. And this man Pilate — he does not deserve to sit in my grandfather's seat. What has he ever done for Israel? What does he know? He is a tragedy for the people. I should be there!'

"Alexander was surprised at the emotion Agrippa displayed as he spoke; this was something that had evidently been growing in him since his youth. But then Alexander said 'What about Herod Antipas? Surely he has a more solid claim on the kingdom than you do.'

"Agrippa's eyes flashed and he said with anger. 'Don't mention that monster's name to me. If he ever got control of the kingdom, I would have to flee for my life or he would find a way to destroy me. No, I am the one for that position.'

"Alexander tried to bring him back to reality. He said, 'But look at your life! So far, you have accomplished nothing, and you have nothing.'

" 'Don't be too sure of that,' said Agrippa. 'Don't forget that I was the best friend of Caesar Tiberius's son. It is true that, out of sorrow and depression, he has refused to see me, but that will pass and he will remember that he once looked on me as a son. He will do that again, and a word from him will put me on top. If circumstances turn out right, I could be one step from the throne.'

" *'He means this!'* thought Alexander. *'Is it possible that this could happen?'*

"Agrippa saw the thoughtful look on Alexander's face, and decided that this was the moment to make his request. 'You are my friend, Alexander, and you were a trusted friend of my mother. I think you are in a position to help me achieve my goal, and help Israel to regain the glory of the kingdom once more. All I need is enough money to get to Rome and live there for one year. In that time I know I can work things out with Tiberius and change the course of history. Help me, Alexander!'

"Alexander hesitated. Agrippa would need a great deal of money to live for a year, and once he got his hands on that money, it would slip through his fingers, and the money would be gone before anything substantial could be accomplished. He would have to do something for him, but a wrong move here might bring him to ruin. Then he looked at Cypros; she was tense, her hands so tightly clasped in her lap that her knuckles were white. What would be best for her? And they had two children with them: Agrippa II who was about eight, and Bernice who was just a babe in arms. What would happen to them if Agrippa continued to travel continually?

" 'Give me a moment to think," he said, and leaned back, closed his eyes, put his fingertips together and was silent. It would be hard to say whether he was thinking or praying. Agrippa watched him closely; he felt his whole future hung in the balance. If Alexander did not give him some money, he could not even move on. Cypros closed her eyes and prayed. She did not know what to ask; there did not seem to be a good answer to her problem.

"After a while, Alexander cleared his throat and said, 'Here is what I am prepared to do.' Agrippa sat up straight — hopeful, fearful, like a man standing before a judge who is about to decide his fate. Alexander said, 'Agrippa, you should not drag your wife and children around with you since you have no idea where you will live, or even if your mission has any chance of success. You could all be stranded in some far-off place with no help. This is not fair, not right. I think Cypros and the children should go home to her father until you see whether God will prosper your enterprise. They will be safe, and you will be free to pursue whatever opportunity opens up for you. What do you think?'

"Agrippa looked at Cypros and asked her simply, 'What do you think?' Cypros had been surprised by the suggestion; she had not even considered it as an option, but it was a good solution to her part of the problem. She looked hopeful, so Alexander said, 'I will be glad to cover your expenses until your husband gets situated.' Cypros felt that this was God's answer to her prayer, so she said, 'Yes, I would like that.'

"Then Alexander turned to Agrippa and said, 'I do not know if you are doing the right thing, but you must bear the responsibility for your own life and your own decisions. I am prepared to go down to the ship with you and pay your fare to Rome, and give you enough money to live frugally for half a year. If God prospers your journey, that will be enough; if not, you will have to make your own way.'

"Agrippa was satisfied; he had hoped for more, but these arrangements would make it possible for him to work his plan. The next day he was on a ship bound for Rome. Cypros left for home a few days later. They had begun a new chapter."

12

"I suppose it will be a short chapter today," said Livy as he settled in for another session.

"Why do you say that?" asked Castor, looking up in surprise.

"Well, you told me that Agrippa did become king of the Jews, and Tiberius was the only one who could give him that honor, so I just figured it all out — he wrote to Caesar asking to see him, Caesar said yes, they made up their differences, and the deed was done. Am I right?"

"Not quite. You forgot that Agrippa carries the seeds of self-destruction with him, and also the baggage of the past, and Agrippa's baggage was heavy and almost crushed him. And I have to tell you that Tiberius never gave him anything!"

"More of the twisted strands?" asked Livy. "Good! That is what makes history so interesting. I'm ready if you are."

Castor was ready. He was enjoying this project and found himself thinking ahead and preparing his material in his mind so it would be in the right order when Livy came.

Although he did not tell Livy this, he made notes of things he wanted to include to make his account as accurate and complete as possible. So he began.

"Agrippa stood by the rail of the ship and watched the waters of the Great Sea slip by. Even with a favorable wind, their progress seemed slow for one so anxious to have great things come to pass in his life. There was nothing he could do about it, and that bothered him. It always bothered him when he could not control the circumstances around him; it made him feel unsure, vulnerable, at the mercy of others who did not always have his interests at heart, or even worse, were plotting against him. So, although the day was pleasant and the sea calm, he felt uneasy and spent much of his time pacing the deck or tossing on his bunk.

"Over and over in his mind, he composed the letter he was going to write to Caesar, wondering how it would sound to him, wondering if

Caesar's suspicion would extend to him and leave him without any help. He had to remind Caesar of the close relationship he had had with Drew, the son that was murdered, but this could be dangerous for him. He had to take the chance. He had to be received back into Caesar's friendship. Without that, his prospects were dim. Once within that circle, he could expand; friends of Caesar are welcome in many places. Right now, all of his skills had to go into this letter. It had to be successful! By the time he landed in Rome, the letter was ready and he sent it on its way. There was nothing he could do now but wait for a reply.

"Tiberius was still on the isle of Capri and even pressing business in Rome could not persuade him to leave. He was living in the villa that Augustus had built overlooking the bay of Naples, and the beautiful weather, the spectacular scenery, and its isolation — three miles from shore — suited Tiberius just fine, and he determined that he would never return to Rome. The day Agrippa's letter arrived, the sun was shining brightly and the cooling sea breeze blew gently through the patio. Tiberius had already consulted his astrologers, and they had given him a favorable reading. Not many things had been favorable for him lately; he was ill, and his physicians did not offer much help. Some of the cures they prescribed were worse than the disease. He was in a gloomy mood most of the time, but this day he felt a little better. If Agrippa had been able to choose a day for his letter to arrive, he could not have done better.

"When Tiberius was ready for the business of the day, his steward, a man named Tasso, brought in a handful of papers. On top was the letter from Agrippa. Seeing the pile in his hand, Tiberius sighed and said, 'All of this business wearies me. Why can't they take care of things without sending them to me? Must I do everything?' Tasso made no reply to the complaint — he heard it nearly every day. He wanted to start the session on a positive note, so he said, 'My Lord, here is a letter from Agrippa. He begs your permission to come and see you. After this long absence, he wants your friendship.' So much for a carefully composed letter — Tiberius did not even look at it, and he did not read a word. Since he was silent, Tasso turned to the next paper in his hand.

"Then Tiberius said in a wistful voice, 'Agrippa...? I wonder...' Tasso could see that he was thinking, so he waited in silence. Finally Caesar said, 'Yes. Tell him to come. My grandson, Tiberius, is young and has much to learn if he is to take over the empire when I am gone. I do not have the time to spend with him, but Agrippa could be his mentor. Yes, yes, tell him to come.'

As Castor was telling this, Livy's eyes brightened almost as though he were saying, "See, I told you so! I knew this was the way it was going to happen." Castor smiled to himself; he was hoping for that reaction. It would make the next turn even more dramatic.

"That afternoon, Tasso sent the dispatch to Agrippa. He was overjoyed, and wasted no time; he set out for Capri at once.

"But Agrippa's past was also pursuing him. The day after Caesar had received his letter, he received another, this one from Governor Capto. In careful military terms, it told of Capto's attempt to recover the three hundred thousand pieces of silver owed Caesar's treasury by Agrippa, and how he had escaped in the night and was now fleeing Roman justice. That morning Tiberius was not feeling well and said to Tasso, 'When he arrives here, throw him in prison until he pays all!' Tasso did not reply and made no move to leave. Caesar sensed his hesitation and said, 'You think I am too harsh with him?' Tasso replied quietly, 'He could help you with young Tiberius.' Caesar thought for a moment and then said, 'I suppose he could, but I am afraid that the first thing he will teach him is to spend all of his money. No, he cannot see me until he has paid his debt. Tell him that when he comes. We will see how he handles that.'

"Agrippa boarded a small boat for the last part of his journey, and his heart beat a little faster as he neared the isle of Capri, rising steeply out of the sea. This day would be a turning point in his life, he was sure; from now on, his fortunes would improve. He announced his arrival at the gate and was figuring out his best greeting for Caesar after the long absence. Imagine his surprise when Tasso sent out the message that Caesar would not receive him until he had settled the debt he owed.

" 'Money again!' he said in anger as he made his way down the hill to the dock. 'Every time a door opens for me, it is slammed shut because I don't have the money. What can I do now? I can as easily fly to the moon as get my hands on three hundred thousand pieces of silver. And soon the money Alexander gave me will run out, and I will be a beggar on the streets of Rome.'

"That night he began to face his problem more realistically, and for him, it always came down to this: 'Who do I know that will lend me money?' His whole life seemed to turn on this question, and he faced it again. 'This is my most critical situation,' he said to himself as he tossed on his bed, but, of course, he had said that many times before. He slept fitfully, and by morning, only one name came to mind as a possibility. That name was Antonia."

"Antonia?" asked Livy. "Do you mean the mother of our present emperor?"

"The same," replied Castor. "She was Tiberius's sister-in-law, and also had been the best friend of Agrippa's mother. She was such an honored woman that even Agrippa did not feel free to approach her to beg for money. 'No,' he thought to himself, 'I will have to find some other source of help. I cannot face that embarrassment.' But it finally came down to it that he had to face that embarrassment. He couldn't think of anyone else to approach. He had no choice.

"Antonia was sorry to hear of his plight — sorry because she could see that he had not corrected this pattern of life that plagued him and hindered him at every turn. Another lecture would do him no good. But could she refuse to help him? That would, no doubt, destroy him. She thought of Bernice, his mother, and decided, rightly or wrongly, she had to help him over this hurdle. 'Here is the three hundred thousand,' she said, 'and a small token besides, but Agrippa, this is the last time. You cannot go on living this way.'

"Agrippa took the money, and was truly thankful, just as he did and was so many times before. He left with a light step and a happy heart, almost singing. At the door he met Gaius, Antonia's grandson. They exchanged words of greeting and small talk, and eventually Gaius invited Agrippa to eat with him. That chance meeting at the door changed the course of history for Agrippa and also for Israel."

Castor got up out of his chair and walked to the small table in the corner of the room and picked up the ornate pitcher and poured himself a goblet of water. He slowly sipped the water as he walked to the window that overlooked his garden. Livy finished his notes and assumed that the session was over, but when he started to rise, Castor said, "Wait, Livy, I am not through yet. I have several threads in my hand now, and if I take too long on this part of the story, we will lose our perspective. I am just trying to figure how much I need to tell and how much to leave out."

He set the goblet aside and resumed his seat. Then he said, "Let me make an attempt at this. Well, first, Agrippa took care of the debt and got to see Tiberius. If Agrippa had hoped for a joyous reception, he was disappointed; but at least, he was back inside the circle. Agrippa was not happy with the prospect of being the mentor to young Tiberius; he did not tell Caesar this because he realized that the relationship was still tenuous, and Caesar could change his mind at any time without warning. He made it a point to be seen in Caesar's company and to be identified as one in royal favor, because he still had a money problem. He had to get his hands on some cash; one cannot eat royal favor. He made a few discreet inquiries and learned of a man who was a prominent money-lender, and made sure that he learned of his favored position in Caesar's household. At the appropriate time, he approached him with an audacious request; he asked for the loan of one million pieces of silver! To his great and happy surprise, the man agreed! He was now a rich man — on borrowed money, of course. He repaid Antonia, and when she asked the source of the money, he was very vague, and she hoped that there was nothing illegal about the acquisition. He then installed himself in a rented villa, hired servants, bought a fine chariot and some excellent horses. To the casual observer, he was just up to his old spendthrift ways, but it turned out that he had something more basic in mind.

"I will say this much for Agrippa," said Castor in a thoughtful mood. "He was a shrewd judge of character and was able to pick a winner long before there were any outward signs to indicate the way history would turn. In this case, he ignored young Tiberius even though Caesar had given him orders to care for him and had restored his friendship especially for that purpose. With Gaius, it was quite the opposite; he used his newfound wealth to lavish rich gifts on him and entertain him in a royal manner. And too, he spent time and attention on Claudius, a man mostly ignored by others — some called him an idiot — because he stammered, had an uncontrollable shaking of the head, and walked like a drunk man. Now you can understand that his judgment was shrewd; that man is our emperor now.

"Although Claudius seemed an unlikely candidate for fame and high honor, Gaius, on the other hand, seemed to be the perfect aspirant. I have called him Gaius, but he was known mostly as Caligula, 'Little Boot.' He got this nickname as a boy. His father, Germanicus, was commander in the north country, and little Gaius dressed like a Roman soldier and wore little boots. He was their mascot and was loved by all. He enjoyed this attention, but at the same time, he learned to get along with people in all stations of life, and was as much at home with the officers as the soldiers in the field. His character was flawless, and even as a lad, he inspired the loyalty of the soldiers to the extent that they would willingly die for him."

"Wait a minute!" called Livy. "I have heard that Caligula was a monster and that there was a great rejoicing at his death. Is this the man you are talking about?"

"Yes, it is. Wait until I come to that part of the story.

"One fine day, Agrippa and Caligula went out for a ride in his chariot. Agrippa's servant, a man named Ute, was the driver. You may think it strange that I mention the name of a driver, but you will see that this man almost destroyed Agrippa before he unfolded his plan.

"As they rode along, they talked of many things, but eventually the future of the empire became the subject of discussion, and Agrippa began to voice some strong opinions about Tiberius. 'I wish the old man would hurry up and die; we would all be better off without him. I can't wait until you take over and do something worthwhile for Rome.' Of course, Caligula enjoyed hearing such flattery and encouraged him to say more. When the afternoon ride was over, they went home and thought no more of it.

"The next day, Agrippa discovered that some of his very valuable clothing was gone, and after making a few inquiries, he learned that Ute had been seen sneaking away under the cover of darkness carrying a large bundle. Agrippa concluded, rightly, that Ute was the thief and sent out word that he should be apprehended and returned. He was apprehended in a short time, but he was not returned. He told the centurion in charge that he had information about a plot against the life of Caesar and would speak only to Caesar himself. The centurion did not take this lightly; information of this kind received the highest priority, so Ute was placed in prison and Tiberius was informed of the matter.

"I think I told you that Tiberius always put off business until he was pushed to attend to it, so Ute stayed in prison for some time. But Agrippa wanted his possessions returned, and not knowing of the other matter, pushed for a trial. He kept at it until Caesar finally agreed, but instead of talking about the items that had been stolen, Ute talked about the conversation in the chariot and what Agrippa had said, and perhaps he added a little to it for emphasis.

"When Tiberius heard this, he was angry. He called a centurion to summon Agrippa. Caesar pointed at him and commanded, 'Bind that man!' The centurion looked at Agrippa in his royal robes and thought he had surely misunderstood, so he did not comply. This time Tiberius's command was more vehement! 'Bind him! Pay no attention to his fine robes. Treat him as harshly as any other criminal — no harsher. He has ignored my orders to serve my grandson, and he is praying for me to die. Feed him bread and water, and let him sleep on the stone floor. Never let him out!'

"What a predicament he was in now! However, Caligula went to see the centurion in charge and asked him to show some kindness to Agrippa, as much kindness as he could show without directly violating the orders of Caesar. His friend also saw to it that he had some decent food.

"Now let me pull a few of these threads of history together because they are about to take a turn. Let's look at the people I have been telling you about and see where they are. Herod Antipas is now in Jerusalem with Vitellius — waiting for the Roman army to march around the borders of Israel so they can attack Aretas, king of Arabia. Pilate is on a ship headed for a meeting with Tiberius to stand trial for his crimes against the people of Samaria. And Agrippa, still in his fine robes, is sleeping on the stone floor of a prison.

"But Caesar Tiberius is ill, and about to die, and that will affect them all."

13

"I am pleased with the way this history is unfolding," said Livy at the next session. "So much intrigue involving so many people throughout the empire, but now I can see the basic theme through it all. Caesar holds the key to history. He determines who rules in Israel, and whoever rules there is controlled by one thought: 'I must please Caesar or I am out.' "

"You are certainly right about that," replied Castor. "And you will see this even more clearly as I continue. It may seem like I am spending a lot of time telling about the events outside the borders of Israel, but I will show you how this affected everyone who lived within its borders. In a way, the death of Tiberius started a completely new chapter in the history of the world, especially for Israel. But first I have to tell you what happened just before his death.

"As I have said, Tiberius was ill and he got progressively worse until he, himself, knew he did not have long to live. There was one more thing he had to do, one more grand, important thing: He had to name his successor, he had to pick the person to hold the most powerful, influential position in the whole world. Now you will see something of the absolute power of Caesar. How would he make the choice? Would he call in the leaders of the Roman senate? Would he consult the commanders of the army? Would he talk to an inner circle of trusted advisers? No! He did none of these things. He consulted his astrologers, and then prayed to his family gods. He was perplexed by the problem; he had no sons, so his nearest relative was his grandson, Tiberius, and he was young. Would the responsibility of the empire crush him? More likely, others would take advantage of him and take away his power. But the other option was no better. Caligula was his brother's son, but he did not trust him. He suspected that he shared Agrippa's desire to have him out of the way, and he had even taken steps to make sure that Caligula did not hasten his demise. No, Caligula would not do; it had to be young Tiberius. But it was a hard decision, and he decided that he would leave it in the hands of his gods, and he asked them for an omen. In some way that I do not understand, he got the message that the first one to greet him the next morning would be the choice of the gods.

"But Caesar was not willing to leave things to chance, so he sent a message to Tiberius's schoolmaster to bring the young man to see him the very first thing in the morning. That was not really fair, but I suppose he just wanted to help the gods make the right choice.

"Early the next morning he said to Tasso, 'Bring in the man who is outside the door, waiting to see me.' Caligula knew nothing about this but just happened to be passing by, so Tasso called to him. 'Caligula, Caesar is ready to see you now.' The reason the schoolmaster had not brought young Tiberius was that he found him at breakfast, and the young man said, 'There is no rush; let him wait until I have finished my breakfast.' His breakfast cost him the empire!

"When Tiberius saw Caligula, he was distressed and told him very frankly, 'I did not want the kingdom to fall into your hands, but now I have no choice because the gods have made the decision. Now I fear for young Tiberius; I am afraid that you will do away with him as soon as I am gone.'

"Caligula replied, 'Do not fear for him; I will take care of him.' Later, when young Tiberius was found murdered, Caligula said that he had never promised that he would keep him alive; he had only said that he would take care of him, and he certainly did!

"Two days later, Caesar died after ruling for more than twenty-two years. Tasso sent the papers to the Roman senate certifying that Caligula was now the emperor, and requiring all to take an oath of allegiance to him. You will remember that I told you that when this same order arrived in Jerusalem, Vitellius immediately did so, and consequently called off the campaign against Aretas and sent the soldiers home.

"Caligula accompanied the body of Tiberius to Rome and arranged for a large and elaborate funeral and accorded him every possible honor. There was a great deal of public mourning, but most of this was not heartfelt. Especially in later years, Tiberius had been difficult to get along with, and often took out his frustrations on anyone who dared to speak a word against him. This had been especially exaggerated ever since he had learned that Sejanus had betrayed him. He had ordered that he be executed at once, but not only Sejanus, but his wife and children — one was a little girl. Next, he ordered that anyone who had been connected with Sejanus be denounced and executed, and then anyone who had been a friend of his; and remember this, Sejanus had been in charge of the government, and Sejanus had already executed anyone he did not perceive as a friend.

"The massacre went on and on; bodies piled high in the street, and spies were sent to watch to see if any came to mourn for them. One mother came to weep for her son, so she was condemned and executed. The bodies were denied burial; they were thrown into the river, and their fortunes went to Caesar. To avoid this, many who were sure they would be condemned committed suicide to avoid this dishonor and the loss of their property. Now the man who fostered all of this was gone, but because of past circumstances, people were afraid to rejoice openly for fear that this would be used against them in the future. If the truth were told, however, there was a great deal of private rejoicing, and everyone hoped for a brighter future.

"Meanwhile, Agrippa was languishing in prison in chains which were never removed. He had been there for six months without a change of clothes, without an opportunity to shave. He looked worn and haggard and felt worse than he looked. He was used to a life of luxury, and now he was reduced to this! He was truly praying that 'the old man would hurry up and die!' The centurion was sympathetic, but every now and then, a man they did not know came by carefully observing, and they were sure that he was a spy sent by Tiberius to make sure that his command that Agrippa be treated harshly was being carried out. Agrippa's condition was so pathetic that Tiberius must have been pleased with the reports.

"One day one of Agrippa's servants came running down the road, and even before he could catch his breath, he shouted through the bars of Agrippa's cell, in Hebrew, 'The lion is dead!' Hearing the news, Agrippa let out a shout of joy, and raised his arms high as though he had been the victor in some great conflict. The commotion quickly attracted the attention of the centurion, and he demanded to know what was going on. At first, Agrippa was afraid to say anything because, evidently, the news had not been made public or the centurion would have heard it before he did. The centurion turned to the servant and commanded him to repeat his message, which he did, but since the centurion could not understand Hebrew, it did him no good. This gave Agrippa time enough to evaluate his situation to see how he could use the news to his advantage, or at least to minimize his discomfort, so he said plainly, 'Tiberius is dead.'

"The centurion replied, 'I thought as much. When you shouted for joy,

I knew that only one thing could account for that. But you must remember that I am under orders, and I cannot change my treatment of you without a written change of my orders.'

"Agrippa was an aggressive fellow, and was not about to let his advantage slip, so he challenged the centurion. 'You know,' he said in stern tones, 'that both Antonia and Caligula are most distressed at my treatment, and they would be very unhappy if you continued it when it was no longer necessary. I demand that you undo my chains and let me go!'

" 'But I have my orders,' protested the centurion.

" 'And I have influential friends!' replied Agrippa.

"This put the centurion on the spot. After thinking over the situation, he said, 'I will show you as much kindness as I can without disobeying the orders I have sworn to uphold. You know that none of this treatment was my idea. I cannot release you, but I will remove your chains, I will let you eat at my table, and I will give you my own room.' This was a wise decision by the centurion. He could see that the change of authority could put him in a very uncomfortable situation. If Agrippa's fortunes were on the rise, he certainly did not want to be on the wrong side. That night he made Agrippa the guest of honor at supper.

"As they were eating, a messenger arrived with a disquieting message; 'Tiberius is not dead, he will be coming to town tomorrow.' The centurion turned pale. 'What have you done to me?' he shouted at Agrippa. 'If this report reaches Tiberius, it will cost me my life!'

"There was nothing Agrippa could say. All he knew was the word of his servant, and he did not know if his report was accurate. He could not protest when he was put in chains again and led from the room and locked in his cell. 'I did not even get a chance to finish my supper,' he said as he lay on the floor of his dark cell.

"However, late the next day, the news was out, and the centurion himself came to Agrippa's cell to remove his chains again. 'You can understand,' he explained, 'that I had no choice. I do not make the rules; I simply obey them. You cannot blame me for thinking that you had tricked me. You can be sure that I will treat you with kindness until the order comes for your release. I hope, for your sake, that it comes quickly.'

"It was not until later that he understood the reason for this confusion. Agrippa's servant had heard that Tiberius was dying, so he joined the servants of Tiberius in order to be an ear for his master. When he heard the shout, 'Caesar is dead!' he stayed just long enough to hear the loud celebration by the friends of Caligula. With their shouts of triumph ringing in his ears, he ran to be the first with the news. Back at the villa the party continued until a servant rushed in and said, 'Tiberius has revived and is now asking for something to eat!' The noise of the celebration then turned into a stunned silence. 'What shall we do?' asked one of Caligula's friends. 'If he has heard the celebration, no doubt he will have all of us put to death.' Caligula did not hesitate long. 'Pile some bedclothes on his face and hold them there! It is not right that he should suffer any longer.' No one really knows if he died a natural death, or if he died that day by suffocation."

Castor looked at Livy and saw the pain on his face; he had been hoping to write a noble Roman history, but it was far from that. Israel had real reason to complain of its treatment, but what had happened to the leading families of Rome had been far worse. Livy looked up from his wax tablet and said, "I hope the story gets better from now on; if it doesn't, I don't see how the empire can survive."

"I cannot tell you about the survival of the empire," said Castor, "but I can tell you that the story does not get better. Many had hoped that Caligula would turn things around. His grandmother, Antonia, had a long talk with him after the funeral. As I have said, she was a noble woman, and deeply concerned for the conditions she saw around her. She knew Caligula respected her, and so she decided that she should try to turn the course of history and steer this raging river into a reasonable, peaceful channel. When they sat down to talk, she began to weep. Caligula was surprised at this, and at first thought she was sad because he had been chosen instead of young Tiberius. 'No,' she said, 'I am weeping for the sorrow of Rome, and for all the blood shed in her streets. This river of blood has not consecrated the stones, but has turned them into monuments of shame which will testify against us for the ages to come. And I weep, not only for the blood that was shed, but also for the river of evil that flows just under the surface, barely hidden from view. The source of that evil river was Caesar Tiberius himself. Some believe that he retired to Capri because he did not want to be bothered with the business of the senate; that part is true, but that is only a part of the story. He retired to Capri so he could practice his disgraceful orgies without being discovered.

"Caligula caught his breath at this revelation, and then said, 'That explains it. I saw some signs of this, but I did not believe it. Yes, I can see it now.'

"Antonia continued: 'I say this with bitter shame, and I would say nothing at all, but I want you to know the depths of his depravity with the hope that you will have the character and integrity to redeem the moral fortunes of Rome so we can hold our heads high and be proud to be Romans. Tiberius's lust was for children — young boys and girls — and he had a team of servants who scouted them, looking for those who were especially beautiful, and preferably aristocratic, and they were brought to Capri for Tiberius to use. These servants were part of this awful shame, but no doubt, by now, they have fled, taking their secrets with them. O Caligula, be noble; be just; let history record that there was at least one Roman emperor who lived a virtuous life and died after lifting the empire to glory, and was truly mourned by his people.'

"During another conversation Caligula mentioned that he was planning to have Agrippa released from prison and was going to ask him to join him in Rome. Antonia's advice was unexpected. She told him, 'Do not take any action hastily. There has been too much change and upheaval, and the best thing you can do is show the people that, although you are young, you take the time to think things through before acting. People know that Agrippa was imprisoned by direct orders from Tiberius, and some may think that you are seeking to dishonor his memory if you reverse his orders too quickly. Certainly, he should be brought out of his miserable conditions, but you could solve the problem by letting him go home under official house arrest. This would disarm the critics and put people at ease.'

"Soon after that, the order came to the centurion and Agrippa was allowed to go home. Along with the order came a one-word message from the new Caesar: 'Patience.' 'I guess I have no choice,' said Agrippa who was not known for his patience. 'I hope he does not forget me in the midst of all the confusion and splendor of Rome. I would hate to spend the rest of my life sitting in a villa in Italy. I must fulfill my destiny.'

"Caligula did not forget him. Two months later, a royal procession, complete with a large contingent of soldiers, arrived at the gate of Agrippa's villa, and Caligula approached Agrippa and embraced him warmly. 'I come to fulfill my promises and share my good fortune,' he said. 'I have gifts for you.' He motioned to a servant who brought a heavy gift wrapped in scarlet cloth. When the cloth was folded back, Agrippa saw a chain, the same size and length he had worn in prison, but this chain was of gold. Caligula clapped his hands and called for the second servant who bore a smaller package. Caligula unwrapped it and held it up for Agrippa to see. It was a crown of gold. Carefully he placed it on Agrippa's head and said, 'I proclaim you king of your late uncle Philip's kingdom!'

"Agrippa was overcome with surprise and gratitude. The honor and wealth had come suddenly, without warning. He had hoped for something, but to receive a kingdom, and even more importantly, to receive the title of king in such a short time, left him speechless. No one had held the title of king in Israel since his grandfather had died. Wealth and fame had been handed to him all at once. His days of poverty were over. If he could gain this much in one day, what would be his by skillful planning in the future?"

Castor stood up and stretched; he had come to a good stopping place. Then he said, "Wait! I ought to say a word about Herod Philip whose kingdom now belonged to Agrippa. You will remember that Herod the Great divided the kingdom into three parts and Philip was given the northernmost part. Since it was so remote, it was not touched by much of the turmoil that afflicted the rest of the country. Philip was also the noblest of Herod's sons and ruled his people with justice and generosity. Capernaum was just south of his border, and the centurion stationed nearest to me told me that his job was an easy one. Philip worked closely with Rome so there was peace and stability. He beautified the city of Caesarea Philippi, but beyond that, did very little building. If you were writing a history of that area and Philip's reign, you would have some good things to say, but it would be a very dull story.

"Oh, and I should tell you that Philip had married Salome, the same one whose dance cost John the Baptist his head, but her dancing days were over, and they lived a quiet, uneventful life. Philip died leaving no children, and Salome married a cousin who ruled a small area in the hills of Lebanon. There, I think that finishes that part. Next time we will finally get back to Israel."

14

"Now let me see if I can remember where we were in the story," said Livy. "Herod Antipas and Vitellius were in Jerusalem waiting for the Roman army to march around the borders of Israel because the elders would not allow the Roman ensigns, which looked like idols to them, to enter their borders. Aretas, king of Arabia, had defeated Herod's attempt to regain his captured city, which prompted Herod's call for help from Rome. Then Caesar Tiberius died, and Vitellius had to take the oath of allegiance to Caligula. Since he then had no authorization for the war, he had to disband the army and send them home. Is that right?"

"That's fine," said Castor. "I had talked to my friend Zebedee about these proceedings, pointing out to him that, if they had been a little more flexible in their rules, the battle would have been over. Zebedee agreed, but he was not in favor of relaxing what appeared to be divine commands to obtain personal ends. 'It is easy,' he told me solemnly, 'to make divine commands mean whatever pleases us, but this is dishonest and will move us outside the protection of the will of god. Besides, who says that Herod, the prophet killer, deserves any victory or special concession from the Almighty?' But now, let me continue.

"It was a disappointed Herod Antipas who returned to his capital city of Tiberias. Caesar had died at a very inconvenient time for him. In many ways, his hopes had been dashed. In his fondest dreams, he had pictured himself as the new king of Arabia with a sizable extension of his kingdom, and he had anticipated the joy of humiliating his old enemy, Aretas, and at the same time, proving to his ex-wife that he was a mighty man, one to be reckoned with. All of this evaporated, had disappeared like a puff of smoke in the breeze when that royal message came. Now he was back where he started — no, not even there. He had one more failure on his record, and the threat to his southern border remained. If he had been able to come home victorious, Herodias would have given him more respect, and he certainly would have felt better about himself.

But all of that was over. Why couldn't Caesar have lived at least long enough for him to gain his victory?

"One day soon after, a caravan of twenty-three camels arrived at the city of Tiberias. The leader, a distinguished-looking Arab named Amir, announced his arrival to the Roman centurion's station, and Julian came out to make sure that everything was in order. Looking at the papers, Julian said, 'I see that you are on your way to Damascus.' Amir adjusted his elaborate headdress showing, perhaps deliberately, the expensive rings on his fingers, and then, speaking in a low, melodious voice replied, 'Yes, if it is the will of God, that will be our destination.'

" 'And the cargo you are carrying?' asked Justin, although he held the bills of loading in his hands.

" 'The usual items gleaned from the far reaches of the desert which are desirable and needed in the cities to the north.' Amir knew that he would not have had to be more specific because the contents of each saddlebag and trunk were clearly listed. Amir did not have to resort to subterfuge to make his money; he carried what people would pay dearly for — cinnamon, frankincense, gold, precious stones, and even some copper and iron.

"I would not mention this encounter nor would Justin have told me about it except for one thing — Amir had just come from Petra. When Justin heard that, he realized that this man had a great deal of information, and if it did not compromise his position in Arabia, he would be willing to share it. And he did.

" 'I was in the rose-red rock city of Petra,' he said in measured tones. 'I was walking down the street and his majesty, the king, was beside me. I had debated about entering the city because of the threat of invasion by the Roman army, but the word I got was that they were some distance off, and I planned to be on my way inside of Israel before they approached. But there was fear in Petra, let me tell you. Warriors had gathered from remote camps in the desert and planned to take up posts in the narrow mountain passes and treacherous valleys, but there was a general agreement that, at best, they could only delay the inevitable defeat. They knew that the most impregnable fortress in the world could not hold out the Roman army for long.

" 'As I said, we were walking down the street when a runner came with the news that Rome had given up the expedition. Aretas immediately called for a celebration, and the people filled the streets, and the stone temples rang with the sounds of singing and dancing. The soothsayers reminded the king that they had prophesied that the Romans would not be able to take Petra, but the king was not sure that the circumstances matched the prophecies. He was happy with the outcome, nevertheless. As word spread to the guarding outposts, more and more warriors arrived, and the celebration went on for days.' "

Castor leaned over and said to Livy, almost confidentially, "Now came the delicate part. Could they find out from Amir what the king of Arabia was planning to do now? Would he continue his threat, or even increase it now that Rome was out of the picture? Had this last event frightened him enough to make him content to stay within his borders?

" 'I joined in the celebration as well,' said Amir. 'Peace is essential to my trade, and after this experience, I am sure that Aretas will think twice before he starts another incursion into Herod's territory.'

" 'That's good news for us,' said Justin, but then he eyed Amir closely and said, '… and after he thinks twice …?'

"Amir smiled. 'Do you want my honest opinion? His hatred for Herod has not cooled; if anything, it has been fanned by this experience. I think he would figure that Herod could not call on Rome for effective help for a long time, and some of his cities are far to the south, impossible to defend against attacks from the desert. If I were Aretas…but I'm not, and I am a man of peace.' Then Amir smiled and bowed, giving indication that he had said all he was going to say and leaving the conclusion for others to figure out.

"When Herod heard of this conversation, his fear soared. He was even more pessimistic about his chances for peace. 'He beat me once,' he said. 'He will try again; and the man is right, I cannot count on Rome for help. I must defend myself and my kingdom with my own forces.'

"That sounded like a reasonable decision, and Justin made no comment about it, and indeed, gave it very little thought. It would be hard to imagine that this decision could prove to be his undoing.

"Herod's first thought was that he had to defend himself from an attack on his southern flank; but then he thought again. Why should he just sit and wait for an attack? Why should he just try to defend himself? If Rome wouldn't help him, he would take care of his own problems; he would extend his own empire by taking over the cities to the south. Caesar should be pleased with that. Then he wondered what other targets would be available to him if he had an invincible army at his command, what greatness would accrue to him, what sense of glory and power would be his!

"That decided it; he had to have an invincible army. He was now convinced that his previous loss was due to the fact that he had insufficient forces to do the job. Vitellius had told him as much during the talks they had in Jerusalem. Thinking about the ensuing battle, Herod had asked him, 'What are our chances of success?' Vitellius looked at him and laughed. 'Chances for success? Ha! We will capture the objective, I can assure you. All that is needed for success is a good battle plan and sufficient resources. It's as simple as that!'

"Herod was not so sure. He had been humiliated before in the same situation. He thought of the reports of his troops fleeing in panic, dropping their weapons and running in all directions. He did not want to mention this — it was too painful to admit — but it bothered him, so he said, 'But what if your troops do not follow the battle plan? You said nothing about execution.'

" 'Of course I didn't,' replied Vitellius. 'In the Roman army, there is no question. From the first day, the men are taught discipline, and when an order is given, it is obeyed — always! We are talking about the Roman army!' He said this with such pride that Herod felt a thrill of expectation; it felt good to have such a force working on his behalf.

"Now he was beginning to formulate a grand plan in his mind. He would be afraid of no man. He would have an army — a large army, well-equipped and especially well-trained, and he would use the plan Vitellius had planned to use. He would become well-known as a military genius! The thought excited him!

"First he would need equipment, a lot of equipment. He decided that he would arm seventy thousand men. What an army! Immediately he set out to secure what was needed: helmets, shields, armor, swords, spears. Nothing like this was available in Israel, so he sent his agents in search of sources. They were successful in Syria, but especially in Parthia. He had more success than he had expected. It was going to work!

"Meanwhile, in Rome, Agrippa was planning his triumphal entry into his new kingdom. When his uncle Philip had come north, there had been very little fanfare and a bare minimum of excitement; in fact, there had been very little excitement during his whole reign. It would not be that way for Agrippa. All the kingdom would know that a new day had dawned, and his return would signal the auspicious beginning of a glorious reign. Expense would be no impediment. After all, he was king, not some petty governor.

"His plans were abetted by Caligula who felt that his glory was somehow enhanced by the advancement of his friend. Rome loved parades and elaborate displays, so Agrippa's return began in Rome with a march from Palatine Hill. Caligula and Agrippa rode in a chariot near the head of the procession, and that led Agrippa to remark about the last time they had ridden together. 'Much has happened since then,' said Agrippa, 'and the thing I had hoped for has come to pass. Now you are the supreme ruler over all of the civilized world. May your rule be long and prosperous!'

"Caligula was savoring this moment of adulation and praise from the cheering throngs. The words of Agrippa thrilled him, and he began to feel that he was destined for greatness, that the world had never seen such a glorious ruler as he would be. He thought, 'I will be loved by my people; no — more than that, I will be adored; no — even more than that, I will be worshiped as a god!' At this thought, a wave of exultation and a feeling of euphoria swept over him such as he had never known. The cheers of the crowd now sounded more joyful and he felt surrounded by a halo of glory. Agrippa was speaking to him, but he did not hear; he was lost in his own visions of grandeur.

"Agrippa's return began in Rome but it did not end there; Caligula had decreed that a Roman cohort of nearly five hundred men as well as one hundred and twenty cavalrymen should accompany him all the way home. Any spectator would conclude that this was the procession of some great conquering hero, the winner of great battles. One would never suspect that the display was accorded to a man who had been on the run to escape his creditors and had slipped away under the cover of darkness to avoid arrest. It is hard to imagine that any man had ever experienced such a change in such a short period of time. The criminal was returning as king.

"When Agrippa's ship and entourage arrived at Caesarea, the whole city turned out for the celebration. Macro had just been appointed governor of Judea by Caligula, and he was anxious to stage a military display of the glory of Rome. The harbor, which enclosed part of the sea, was ablaze with banners waving in the breeze, and soldiers in battle array lined the port. Agrippa's cohort and cavalry led the parade through the city to the Roman camp, and for a week, they had parades, games, and celebrations. People came from miles around to see this, the greatest spectacle in years.

"News of this great event reached Tiberias, and when Herod heard of it, he was furious. 'There is no justice in the world,' he cried, waving his arms and shouting at the top of his voice. 'If I had not fed him, he would have starved to death. That's what I should have done!' Then he turned on Herodias and vented his seething wrath on her. 'It's all your fault. I never should have listened to you when you begged me to bring him here. If I had done what I thought was right, he would have died at that tower of his. Whenever I listen to you, I come to grief.'

"Herodias knew that he was still disturbed about John the Baptist, and she resented this. Herod would have been wise not to bring that up at this time; she was already furious that her brother had somehow managed to attain a level of glory that she had dreamed of all these years and had never been able to attain. Herod's words touched a sore spot, and she exploded. 'If you had a little ambition, you could be king, but no — you are too lazy to reach out for anything. You are content to sit here and let the world pass you by. If a fool like my worthless brother can climb the heights so easily, why can't you? Your trouble is that you are too pig-headed to listen to me. I certainly would not have been content with the little position that seems to have satisfied you!'

"This was was just the beginning of the battle. Herodias became more and more unhappy. She even sent spies to see if the reports of Agrippa's wealth were true, and when she heard of all he had, she was so envious that it ate away at her, and everything she had seemed insufficient. She had to have more! She would not be content until she had more than Agrippa! Much more! So she kept at Herod night and day.

" 'You are the son of a king,' she would say to him. "He is the son of a man who was executed because your father thought he was not fit to live. But look at things now! He is king, and you are not. And you never will be! You are too lazy! How do you think he got that honor? He went after it and he got it, unworthy as he is. If you had any ambition, any courage, you would go to Caesar and demand the same honor. But, no! You are content to sit here in this godforsaken place and do nothing. I can't understand you, Herod. I thought you were a better man than this.'

"Herod resisted her for a long time, partly because he was lazy, but also because he was not sure of the reception he would get in Rome. He just did not want to take the chance. But he couldn't resist forever, and finally he was worn down. She was making life miserable for him, so one day, after she had been particularly outspoken, he relented. 'Enough! Enough!' he said in exasperation. 'We will go, but if it turns out badly, it will be your fault.'

"Herodias got what she wanted. 'Yes,' she said, 'I will gladly take full responsibility, and when you are king, remember who it was that got you there.' There was no doubt in her mind that she had made the greatest move of her life. In a short time she would have the thing she had always craved — she would be queen!

"Now Agrippa made it his business to know what was happening in Herod's kingdom; he knew of his growing animosity and he did not trust him. He was concerned about the large army he was building and was afraid that he would decide to make a move against him. He didn't trust Herod at all, and now he was sure that his sister had turned against him as well. When the two started on their way to Rome, Agrippa heard of it, and he knew why they were going. Agrippa decided to make sure that his plan did not succeed. Without delay, he called his chief man, a fellow named Fortunatus, and explained the whole matter to him.

" 'We have a chance to play our advantage,' he explained. 'They will learn that Caligula is a friend of mine, and although they despise me and think I am nobody, they will find out that I have a great deal of influence in Rome. Here, take these letters, and see that Caligula gets them as soon as possible. To have any chance, you have to get them to Caesar before he makes a decision for them.'

"Herod and Herodias had a two-day head start, but travel by sea is very unpredictable, and many things are out of the control of the sailors. The winds were favorable for Fortunatus and he arrived just shortly after Herod and Herodias; in fact, they were having their audience with Caligula when Fortunatus arrived. Herod was expounding on his claim to the title of king, explaining that his father, Herod the Great, had originally decreed that he should have the whole kingdom, but unfortunately, during his last illness, had changed his mind. He told Caligula that now he had an opportunity to rectify that unfortunate mistake. He was son of a king and deserved to be called king.

"Caligula did not like him; he did not like his tone of voice, and he did not like it that this man was telling him what he ought to do. He was about to tell him that he would think about the matter, when a servant came and whispered something into his ear; important letters that demanded immediate attention had arrived from Agrippa. Caligula excused himself and went out to read the information that Agrippa had sent.

"Agrippa had composed a most damaging letter. He had woven a careful blend of truth and fiction that made a damning case against Herod. Agrippa said that Herod was a man who could not be trusted. He claimed that he had been in league with Sejanus in his effort to eliminate the family of Tiberius and leave the Roman senate in charge. This may or may not have been true. Then he said that Herod was raising an army of seventy thousand men and was in league with Arba, king of Parthia, and that they had plans to revolt against Rome and set up a new kingdom. Caligula was only too happy to believe all these things against Herod. Herod's great gamble was about to pay off an ignominious defeat.

"When Caligula left the room, Herod asked his wife, 'What do you think? Will we get it?' Herodias tried to put on a confident front, although inwardly she was worried, but she said, 'We will get what we deserve.'

"When Caligula returned he looked like a thunder cloud. 'So you are preparing an army of seventy thousand men?' he asked menacingly. Herod was caught off guard. He stuttered and stammered, and in his confusion, he heard Caligula shouting at him, 'Answer yes or no! Yes or no!' He thought of denying it, but decided against it. Then he thought he should explain, so he started, 'Yes, but…' He never got beyond that word. Caligula had heard all he wanted to hear, so he held up his hands and demanded silence. Then, trembling with rage and almost uncontrollable anger, he shouted, 'I declare you an enemy of Caesar and sentence you to banishment to Gaul for the rest of your life, and all of your goods and properties are forfeited to Rome!'

"Herod was stunned, speechless. He did not know what to say, and since Caligula had demanded silence, he wouldn't have been able to defend himself even if he had wanted to. His whole life had crashed around him in a moment. He had hoped to be king; now he was an exile with no hope of return. He staggered from the room supported by Herodias.

"Just as they reached the outer door, a servant rushed up to Herodias and said to her, 'Return. Caesar wants to see you.' She turned to follow him and Herod started to go along, but the servant said curtly, 'Not you! You stay here.' This worried Herod, but he was powerless to do anything about it. He feared that Caligula had designs on his wife, and if he did, there would be no aid for him. This thought had not entered Herodias's mind, but she was in such a state of confusion that she was not thinking clearly. She certainly was not prepared for the question Caesar put to her.

" 'Are you Agrippa's sister?' he asked.

"The question brought her up short. 'Yes, I am,' she said, wondering what that had to do with the hard punishment he had just inflicted on them.

"Caligula looked at her and said in a condescending voice, 'In honor of your brother, I am going to allow you to keep your own personal wealth. In his letter, he did not speak against you, so I will presume thatyou are guiltless.'

" 'In his letter?' began Herodias. 'What letter?'

"Caligula replied, 'In this letter' — he held it up and waved it — 'telling of Herod's plot against me.' Herodias saw it all clearly now; it had been Agrippa who had brought about their ruin. Now Caligula was offering her her freedom and her money as a favor to Agrippa.

"She exploded in anger, and shouted some things that under other circumstances would have warranted execution. She was yelling hysterically, calling down the wrath of God on Caligula, on Agrippa, on the whole Roman Empire, declaring that she would die before she took an ounce of his kindness. She was like a wild woman. The guards had already laid hands on her, and with a careless wave of his hand, Caligula sent her out of his presence. Then he did one more thing; he called his scribe and wrote an imperial decree giving all of Herod's territories and wealth to Agrippa.

"What a stunning reversal of fortunes! Who could foresee such a thing? When I went to see Zebedee about this, he said to me, 'Behold the judgment of God, often delayed, but never avoided. This came to them because of what they did to John the Baptist, and because Herod mocked Christ. And that evil woman — when she had a chance to escape some of the judgment, she condemned herself by her anger. But remember this, a Herod, Herod Agrippa, still sits on the throne.' "

Livy saw that the lesson was coming to an end and asked, "Where did they go?"

Castor replied, "They were exiled to Gaul to to the city of Lyon, and for all I know, they are still there. But you will hear no more from them. Their history is finished!"

15

"I sense that we are coming to the end of our story," said Livy as he settled in for the next session. "Both Pilate and Herod are now banished from Israel, and the only person who might cause problems is Agrippa. I must confess that I don't think much of his qualifications for leadership, and it would be my guess that he does not fare very well. Am I right?"

"You are right in your evaluation of Agrippa," said Castor, "but, sad to say, the next wave of trouble, one that threatened to destroy the nation, came from Rome, from Caesar."

"I was afraid of that," said Livy. "I remember Caligula's reputation, and I heard that he poisoned everything he touched. But I thought you told me that he started off so well."

"He did," said Castor, "but that did not last long. I think he had a mental illness that ran in the family, and that illness changed him into a monster. Tiberius was certainly unbalanced, especially at the end, and — you will forgive me for saying this — our present emperor, Claudius, was thought to be an idiot, perhaps because of his stuttering and uncontrollable shaking of his head, and of course, when he walks, he staggers like a drunken man."

"What am I to write?" asked Livy in obvious distress. "Shall I tell future generations that the great Roman Empire was ruled by men who were mentally deficient?"

"You do not need to make medical judgments about them," replied Castor. "Tell the facts, but I am sure that your readers will come to the same conclusions that you have. But now let me tell you how Caligula almost destroyed the nation of Israel.

"The problem began in Egypt, in Alexandria. Although the city is on the African coast, it is actually a Greek city dating back to the days of Alexander the Great. When the Jewish community began to multiply there, tensions arose. There is a natural rivalry between the Greeks and the Jews for several reasons. The Greeks lay claim to being the leaders

114

in the world of philosophy, and the Jews, with their long tradition of prophets, claim leadership in the religious world. But the real clash came in the area of morality. The Hebrews have very strict standards of morality, which is the basis for their religion. But the Greeks worship gods and goddesses which, according to Jewish standards, are immoral, and this causes a violent clash of basic values. It is difficult for morality and immorality to live side by side because each feels threatened by the other.

"The trouble came to a head when the Jewish community expanded and found itself near the Temple of Isis. As you know, Isis is the main goddess of Egypt, and is so much like Venus of the Romans that Isis temples are now found in Rome. The Greeks claimed that Isis was the goddess of love and beauty, and these two qualities represented the best that life had to offer. The Jews resented the temple prostitution, and it came to the point of violence when some young Jewish boys were caught with the temple prostitutes. The boys claimed that they were seduced by them, and the elders were angry and also afraid that the younger generation might be attracted to this heathen religion.

"It is always difficult for two cultures to exist peacefully side by side, and this friction is doubled when religious differences are involved, and one could not imagine any two religions that are more diametrically opposed than these two. The Greeks felt that they had the advantage since their religion was native to the soil of Egypt, and since they also knew that there was an anti-Jewish bias in Rome that had existed since Tiberius had exiled so many, so they decided to go on the attack. Accordingly, they decided to put their case before Caesar and accuse the Jews of being anti-Roman and a present threat to the empire. Caligula agreed to see them, but he warned them, 'I don't want mobs chanting and demonstrating around here. Send me three from each group, and I will give you a decision.'

"When the audience was held before Caligula, a Greek orator named Argos was chosen to present their case. Alexander was chosen by the Jews, and he was the only one of their group that was allowed inside; the others had to wait outside. Argos did a masterful job, playing on Caligula's fears of rebellion on the edges of the empire, and also, perhaps especially, on his desire to receive homage, if not worship, from everyone in the empire. Argos concluded by saying, 'O great Caesar, you yourself be the judge of our quarrel. When we Greeks have a matter to be judged, everyone is required to swear by the name of Caesar that the testimony is true. Ask the Jews, now, here in the very presence of Caesar, if they will take such an oath. Here he paused to make the point more telling. He knew that the Jews would never take such an oath, even to save their lives. Then he went on to his last point. 'We Greeks have a temple in your honor with your statue in it, and offerings are made in your honor. Ask the Jews if, in all of Israel, there is one temple, one image, one place to honor your great name. No. Do not ask them; I will tell you. There is none — not one, in all of their land. And they are the ones who are complaining about our gods. We are willing to accept your wise judgement in this case.'

"Alexander knew that they were in jeopardy. This had always been a sore point with the Roman emperors demanding their allegiance, which amounted to worship, and the Jews refusing because it violated their first commandment. He decided that his only hope was to appeal to Caligula and ask for understanding of their problem in light of their ancient traditions. He rose slowly to speak, but he never got the chance. Caligula began shouting in rage, almost like a crazy man, shaking his fist at Alexander, 'Guards, throw that man out. I will not listen to a man who will not swear by my name or accord me the honor due my person. Throw the traitor out!'

"The other Jews were anxiously awaiting word about the outcome, but when they saw Alexander being so rudely ejected, they knew that they were in danger. Alexander came to them and said, 'Let us return home; it will do no good to stay here in Rome. Only God can save the Jews now from the tragedy which is about to befall us.'

"He was correct in his evaluation of the situation. Caligula was so angry he could hardly speak, but he called his scribe and began to issue imperial commands. 'Vitellias, my emissary to Syria, has known about this problem for years and has done nothing about it. Either he has no courage or else he is a traitor to Rome. Fire him! Tell him he is through and tell him to put Petron in charge. Then tell him to get back here to Rome and answer to me. Now here's what I want you to write to Petron, and make this strong, even with threats! Tell him that I want my image — MY IMAGE — set up in Jerusalem; no, wait — say that I want my image set up in the Temple in Jerusalem, and I want them to worship it. If Argos is right, and I think he is, they will balk at this, and that will reveal their true colors. I hope they do! Then tell Petron this very clearly so that there will be no mistake. Tell him that I want this done without delay, and do it even if it means killing every man, woman, and child in

Israel; and if he has to kill them all until there is no one left in the land, then let him set up the image in the Temple and kneel alone, but I will be worshiped as god in that Temple.'

"You can imagine the consternation this caused when the news reached Israel. It was like receiving a death sentence. Sure enough, Petron came marching from Syria with two Roman legions. When he reached Ptolemaïs, just to the north, he decided to winter there and begin his assault in the spring as soon as the weather would permit. This delay gave the Jews an opportunity to come to Ptolemaïs and make their appeal.

"Petron was unprepared for their approach. He was prepared to deal with them from a position of force, but they did not come with force or threats of violence. Not only did the leaders come from Jerusalem, but elders from all of the towns, including the elder Ezra from Capernaum, came and gathered outside the Roman camp. Along with them came thousands and thousands of ordinary people, and when the commanders saw the sea of people, they put the whole camp on alert and had them prepare for battle.

"Petron would have known how to direct the battle, but he did not know how to deal with what followed. There were no shouts, no upraised fists, no threats; the people stood in absolute silence. When the elders were allowed to see Petron, their request was simple. 'We cannot allow this desecration of our land and of our Temple. If you propose to do this, we beg you to kill us first so that our eyes will not behold this evil thing. We will willingly bare our necks and offer no resistance.'

"Petron was an honorable, reasonable man, and he could clearly see the problem he faced. There was no doubt about Caesar's order, but also there was no doubt that the Jews were serious about their intention to lay down their lives rather than submit to the sacrilege. Petron was the man caught in the middle, and he could not see a way to extricate himself from this impossible spot. So he called the elders to explain his predicament.

" 'I am a reasonable man,' he began, 'and a man of compassion. But you must understand that I am also a man under orders, and I cannot change or modify them in any way. I want you to know that if I were Caesar, I would never make such a demand upon you, but you must also be aware of my situation. If I refuse to carry out the order, Caesar will simply have me executed, and he will replace me with someone who will carry out the order, and perhaps add to it unspeakable cruelty. So you see, we face this problem together. We must find a way to erect the image without causing a terrible loss of life. I beg you to work with me to find a compromise.'

"The elders were moved by his compassion and understanding, and took great pains to praise him and thank him for this. This display of good will lifted the burden from Petron, and he was beginning to hope that they could find an an acceptable compromise. He felt that until an elder from Jerusalem spoke. 'We thank you for your kindness and reasonable spirit. All the world could live in peace and harmony if all the leaders would show such a concern for the people they govern. And we are concerned about your position and your need to obey the orders given to you. If this were some light thing, we, too, would obey, if not out of obedience to Caesar, at least out of respect to you and your kind treatment of us.

" 'But this is not a light matter. Our God gave us commandments when He delivered us out of Egypt long, long ago, and these commandments are more precious to us than life itself. Other things may be open to compromise, but the commandments of God are not. We cannot betray our God. You do what you must; we cannot change!'

"Petron had to find a way to buy some time. He was caught in an impossible situation, so he said to them, 'I will hold an audience in Tiberias to see if it is indeed the will of all of the people to die rather than follow Caesar's order. Then I will make my decision.'

"This he did, and the people came in even greater numbers than before. Capernaum was virtually emptied, so I took my men with me to help keep order in the vast crowd, a crowd of so many thousands that no one could count them all. Agrippa was in Rome at that time, and his brother, Aristo, was chosen to speak to Petron and explain to him that the people would never change their resolve.

"Petron said to Aristo, 'But they should be home preparing their fields so they will be able to plant their crops. If they don't leave soon, they will not be able to plant, and they will starve.'

" 'Then they will starve,' replied Aristo, 'but they will never be persuaded to leave until this matter is settled.'

"After a number of days, Petron could see that this was true, so in great fear, he wrote to Caesar telling him that the order could not be carried out without an insane slaughter of so many thousands of unarmed people that it would be a blot on the honor of the empire for all time to come. He sent the letter, and told the people to go home. All they could do now is wait.

"When Caligula received the letter, he flew into a rage. He immediately shouted for his scribe and said to him, 'Write this in big, bold letters: What do you think should happen to a Roman soldier who refuses to obey the orders of his commander? You know the answer to that! I, Caesar, order you to take your own life with your own sword the day you receive this letter, before the sun goes down!'

"The scribe wrote the letter at once, and a servant hurried it down to a waiting ship, and the order was on its way."

16

"I have been trying to figure this out," said Livy as he sat in Castor's garden. "I know that an imperial command has to be carried out, and I can see no way for Petron to escape the death penalty, but then what happened? As far as I can see, this would only lead to the appointment of a more ruthless general and the slaughter would commence. I have been trying to come up with another solution, but I come up empty."

Castor replied very earnestly, "Then you can appreciate the concern I had in Capernaum. It pained me to consider that my friends would be swallowed up in the coming slaughter, but I knew they would never surrender. But there was more than that to consider. Remember that I was a centurion under army orders. I could see no way to avoid being caught up in this, and personally, I was coming to the same conclusion that Petron had chosen. I would never order my men to slaughter innocent, defenseless people, and it was unthinkable that I should bare my sword against Zebedee, or Sarah, or Alex, or Ezra, or Andrew, or James, or Peter — shall I go on? I had lived with these people; I knew and loved them. I could not escape the conclusion that I would meet my death before they did. It was a very tense time, need I tell you!

"I had made up my mind, but I had to talk to someone; I had to communicate my decision in order to strengthen my resolve. It is not an easy thing to decide to give up your life for a cause, and I could see my whole career, all of my faithfulness to the Roman army, and indeed, my pride in my Roman citizenship, disappearing in a moment. I would be branded a traitor to my own people.

"But there was more than that. Sarah and Alex had been talking to me about their God and about Jesus, the Christ. Deep in my heart I knew the truth of this, but I also knew that the Jew's religion made it impossible for them to serve in the Roman army. I decided to keep my belief secret, but I could see that I was choosing to honor the worship of the God of Israel rather than obey my oath as a Roman centurion. So I went to talk to Sarah and Alex and tell them of my decision.

"They were overjoyed at my decision, but I found that they were less concerned about the situation than I was. Sarah explained, 'Your life is always safe in the will of God. This does not mean that we will not suffer, or even be put to death, but the one who does God's will abides forever. You can be sure that God in heaven is aware of our distress, and if He chooses, He can deliver us all in a moment.'

" 'I wish I shared your optimism,' I replied to her, and in reality, I think I was saying, 'I wish I shared your faith.' Before I left, we prayed especially for me."

As Castor said this, he watched Livy carefully to see what his reaction would be, but Livy just continued to write and showed no sign of surprise, so Castor continued. "More and more I could see the difference between the God of the Hebrew Scriptures and the so-called gods of Rome, and when Caligula, that monster, proclaimed himself a god, that was the end. He went into the main temple of Jupiter in Rome and declared that he was the brother of Jupiter, and when his daughter was born, he took her into the temple and laid her on the knees of the statue and proclaimed that the baby had two fathers — himself and Jupiter — and then he demanded that he should be given equal worship. How can any thinking man take such a thing seriously?

"The Greek religions also suffered at his hands. He went through their temples looking for the finest engravings and statues, and when he found something he liked, he took it home with him, even though it had been consecrated to their gods. In Athens he saw the famous statue of Jupiter Olympus made by Phidias, and demanded that it be sent to Rome.

"In Rome, death came swiftly to those who displeased him or possessed something he wanted. He accused the wealthy without number, and senators, and after having them killed, he took all their possessions."

Livy broke in: "Why didn't the people rise up against such oppression?"

"At times they did. Once hundreds gathered to ask that their oppressive taxes be reduced. They gathered outside of Caesar's palace and voiced their complaints. When Caligula heard the noise, he asked his captain, 'What is all of that disturbance about? Tell them to be quiet; they are disturbing me.' The captain replied, 'They have come here to complain about their high taxes and would like an audience with you. Caesar just laughed and said, 'I do not ask for anyone's advice about taxes, and I will show them what happens to people who complain in the streets of Rome. Send out the soldiers and surround them; then wade in and kill them all — all of them; do you understand?' The captain had no choice but to carry out the order at once, and while Caesar watched from his balcony, the deed was done. That put an effective end to complaints about high taxes, or anything else. But there is also another reason, a deeper reason, one that is an embarrassment to Rome. The common people liked him."

Livy shouted in surprise. "They liked him? How could that be?"

Castor explained. "Often Caesar would stand on his balcony and throw money to the people below. He would also stage great shows lasting for days at a time, and everyone was invited — free — even slaves, but the shows were bloody and cruel. The people did not want to give these up. And the slaves loved him. He gave them the right to denounce their owners for real or imagined offenses, and when they were executed, the slaves received one eighth of all of the wealth. You can imagine what confusion this caused in the city.

"But most of all, his bodyguards prevented it. He was surrounded by a special contingent of Germans who were rough and cruel, and he lavished money and kindness on them so they would be loyal to him, like trained attack dogs. If Caligula heard even a rumor of a conspiracy against him, he would send his guards out to end it. No, it was not easy to rise up against him.

"As Caligula's disease progressed, his cruelty increased. He was no longer content just to kill his opponents; he wanted to see them tortured in the most cruel ways, ways that passed comprehension. He put Shara, the captain of the Praetorian guard in charge of this horrible business, and in a way, this choice finally brought about his downfall. There was a beautiful woman, well-known in Rome, and Caligula ordered her seized and tortured. Like a demented fiend, he demanded more and more torture until this once beautiful woman was pitiful to behold. It was too much for Shara. At the risk of his life, he went to see some senators and said to them, 'If we let this go on, we are just as guilty as Caesar. He is making monsters out of all of us. I am ashamed of myself for what I have done, and I am willing to give up my life to clear this wrong. As Caesar leaves the games, I am going to strike him down. Are you with me?'

"And so Caesar was slain by the leader of the Praetorian guard and Roman senators.

"Back in Israel we were waiting for word from Rome, and the word that arrived was the first message that Caesar had sent demanding that

Petron kill himself. There was grief and sadness, and a cry went up to God for deliverance. And deliverance came! The ship carrying the news of Caesar's death had a rapid journey with favorable winds all the way. Although it did not overtake the message, the second ship arrived so shortly after, that the morning turned to joy. All of the decrees of Caligula were now of no effect. Petron was spared, and the army sent home.

"Now behold the twisted strands of history. As I told you, Agrippa was in Rome at that time, and when he heard of the death of Caligula, he could see that the position and power that he had built up over the years was in danger of collapsing in a moment. He hurried to the palace and found the city in confusion. The German bodyguards were searching for the killers, but they were killing everyone in their path. The senate was meeting in emergency session faced with the real possibility that there would be rioting and looting, but they also feared a military takeover. This was entirely possible because the army did not want the power to pass to the senate; they considered them weak and ineffective and they were sure they would let the empire disintegrate. Agrippa saw his opportunity in all of this confusion. This man, this king from Galilee, stepped in and changed the course of Roman history.

"Caligula's uncle, Claudius, had survived all of the political murders, mostly because people thought that he was mentally deficient and would not be a threat to anyone. When the Germans came searching the palace, Claudius was so frightened he did not know what to do, so he went to his room and hid behind the drapes. There he stood, too frightened to move, while confusion reigned outside. Agrippa had known Claudius since he was a boy at school in Tiberius's court, and he could see possibilities here. Claudius was the only one left of the ruling family, and if Agrippa could manage to have him declared emperor, he would again have a friend in Rome and his position would be secure. Here's what he did.

"First, he went to some senators and told them that the army was preparing to take over the government, and told them that the only way to prevent this was to proclaim Claudius as emperor. He assured them that they would be able to control the government through him and that he was so weak that he would pose no threat to them. Then he went to the army and told them that the senate had already taken control of the situation and if they did not act at once and proclaim Claudius as emperor, they would be the losers in the power struggle. They agreed.

All that remained then, was for Agrippa to find Claudius and bring him out. He went through the rooms calling out, 'Claudius! Claudius! It's me, Agrippa. Come out; there is no more trouble out here.' As he was leaving Claudius's bedroom, he thought he heard a noise and a rustle of the drapes. He pulled them back and there was Claudius, so frightened that he could not move. Agrippa pulled him into the room and told him to put on his finest robe; he told him that he was to be made emperor. This terrified him even more, and when he tried to speak, he could only stammer. Agrippa led him out into the court and there the army proclaimed him emperor and the senate immediately confirmed it."

Livy turned to Castor and said, "Is this the story of Rome? I'm almost ashamed to write this."

Castor smiled at Livy's confusion and said, "As a historian, it is not your business to be ashamed or proud, but to record the facts. But actually, you will have to admit that things have not been as bad under Claudius as they were under Caligula or even Tiberius. But here's the point I want to make here: because of Agrippa's clever political actions, he was richly rewarded by Claudius. Listen to this! Claudius gave Agrippa the territories of Judea and Samaria, making him the greatest king in the east, and now he controlled all the territories that had been held by his grandfather, Herod the Great. He was now truly king of the Jews.

"Soon Agrippa left Rome and did what he had dreamed of doing since he was a boy—he moved into the palace in Jerusalem that had been built by his grandfather who had boasted that he was a greater king than David or Solomon because of the cities he had built and the extent of his kingdom. Agrippa had done nothing yet, but he began telling himself that he would be greater than them all. He would make a name for himself that would live forever! He was not sure how he would do this, but he was sure that he was wiser than the Roman emperors who had given him his position. Already he was beginning to suffer from the malady of kings and emperors — the feeling that he was no mere mortal man, that he was something so special that he ought to be loved and respected by everyone in his kingdom. This would be the golden age of Israel; no enemy would dare threaten, and weak Emperor Claudius would never interfere. Oh, how great he would be!"

"But it did not turn out that way!"

"Alex and Sarah made another trip to Jerusalem to see her father who was old and ill. To their happy surprise, they learned that the two sons of Zebedee, James and John, had made her father's house their home while they were in Jerusalem. The men had not been home to Capernaum for a long time; the affairs of the new church required their time and attention. The church had grown by leaps and bounds, and a short time after its founding at Pentecost, there were thousands of followers. Every day they grew in numbers and influence, and soon the anger and antipathy the leaders had directed at Jesus was turned on them. Persecution began, scattering the followers far and wide. But that was like scattering fire in a dry grain field. It seemed that every town and city, even as far as Rome, had believers meeting on the first day of the week. Seeing this, the priests and leaders decided that they would have to take more drastic action, so they called a council to discuss the problem.

"When they gathered, a Pharisee named Gamus stood up and addressed them: 'Unless we take drastic action, these Christians will fill the whole world with their doctrine and the Jewish religion will cease to exist. See how many priests and Pharisees have joined this heresy already! The more we speak against them, the more they multiply. I propose that we cut the head off the snake, and then it will die by sundown. We must start with the leaders in Jerusalem, and not deport them to spread their mischief elsewhere, but we must kill them. We can do this with the help of King Agrippa. I have talked with him, and he agrees that they are troublemakers and should have no place in our holy land. We should start with the sons of Zebedee and the man called Peter.'

"It was late in the evening, and Alex and Sarah were sitting in the house with James, talking about the changes that were taking place in Capernaum when a sharp knock came at the door. The sound was so loud that it startled them; it was the sound of a sword handle banging against the door. Alex went to the door and opened it; he was immediately seized by soldiers — they were from the Temple guard — and his arms were bound behind him. Then they seized James and bound him as well while two soldiers roughly grabbed Sarah. Then the Pharisee, Gamus, came into the room and said, 'James and John, you are under arrest for treason against our nation and our religion.'

"Alex replied, 'I am not John; you have the wrong man.'

" 'We will see about that,' said Gamus. 'Whoever you are, you are guilty of associating with a criminal.'

" 'And this woman?' asked one of the soldiers.

" 'Bring her along too,' said Gamus. 'We will decide what to do with her later.'

"They were taken to a cell in the Fortress of Antonia where they spent the night, not sleeping, but praying and singing. They were well aware that the next day might be their last on earth, but instead of being filled with fear, they were filled with peace and joy, and the dark prison cell seemed to be a little piece of heaven.

"When the morning came, they were brought before King Agrippa, and Gamus made his speech and concluded by saying they had delayed too long already, and unless all of the leaders were killed, the evil would spread and destroy the nation. Then speaking earnestly to Agrippa, he said, 'We give thanks to God for sending you to us to save our nation. You have the courage and the wisdom to do what is best for us.'

"Agrippa felt a surge of power and importance and he proposed to demonstrate it. 'So here we have James and John...' he began, but Gamus interrupted him and said, 'No, my Lord. We have James who is the ringleader, but this man says his name is Alex and this is his wife. They are from Capernaum, but they admit that they are believers and we found them with James.'

"Agrippa began again, 'James, you are a traitor to our nation and a destroyer of our religion. I sentence you to death!' Then turning to the captain of the guard, he commanded, 'Guard, slay this man!' With a slow, deliberate motion, the captain advanced and stood before James who did not move. With one quick thrust, the captain brought up his sword, striking James under the ribs and piercing his heart. Without a sound, James slumped to the floor. Sarah screamed.

" 'Good job, Captain!' shouted Agrippa. 'You have just struck the first effective blow for the cleansing of our nation. Now make sure that you capture Peter and John and we will do the same to them. Then, one city, one town at a time, we will get rid of this menace.'

"As he turned to go, the captain asked, 'And what about these?' Agrippa had seen that his harsh, decisive treatment of James had met with the approval of the leaders; they saw him as their hero, and he intended to build upon this to enhance his popularity. He looked upon his decision about Alex and Sarah as another opportunity to gain political stature. After only a brief hesitation, he said, 'Beat them with rods — ten strokes each — ten heavy strokes, and do not spare the woman. But be careful that you do not kill them; I want them to carry the message back to Capernaum that Christians have no place in my kingdom.' He left feeling very good about his performance, sure that he had made an excellent impression on the leaders. They would be on his side now; it would be easy to govern with such support.

"When Alex and Sarah were taken to the whipping post, Alex began to plead for his wife. 'Let me take her blows. It is not right or decent that she should be treated this way.'

"The captain retorted, 'You will have all the pain you can handle with your own punishment. No, the order is ten blows each.'

"Again Alex pleaded, 'Then for modesty's sake, let her keep on her robe. It is thin so the rod will still do its damage, but her modesty will be saved.'

"The captain hesitated, and then said, 'The order says nothing about a robe; let her keep it.'

"Then Alex said, 'Let me go first,' but immediately Sarah said, 'No, let me go first; I do not want to see what they will do to you.'

"The captain said, 'The woman will go first,' and although this spared Sarah the pain of seeing her husband beaten, the pain that Alex suffered from seeing his wife tortured was too great to calculate.

"Sarah was led to the whipping post and her arms were tied around it so she could not move. A soldier took a Roman rod and stood in his position waiting for the signal from the captain. The captain shouted 'One!' and the rod whistled through the air and struck Sarah with a thud. She had determined that she would not cry out, but she could not contain the muffled scream that rose up within her. 'Two!' shouted the captain, and the rod fell again. 'Three!' 'Four!' After the fourth blow, no sound came from Sarah, and Alex truly feared that she was dead, but the blows did not stop until the full count had been administered. Mercifully, she did not see the blows that rained down on the bare back of her husband."

Castor got up from his seat and went to the carafe to get a drink. Livy could see that the narration had been hard for him, and he also had the feeling that Castor knew more about the details of the punishment than he was willing to divulge. He had to tell the story, but he would keep the details to himself. Livy thought it best to let it go at that, to ask no questions, and make no embellishments. He waited patiently as Castor composed himself so he could continue his narrative.

17

Livy sat in silence for a while watching Castor and then ventured his opinion, "The future does not look very good for Christians, does it? If Agrippa is committed to destroying them, what can they do? Where can they go? It seems to me that their chances for survival are slight."

"Far from it!" said Castor with enthusiasm. "God is on their side, and they are willing to pay any price, suffer any pain in order to share the message. Let me show you what I mean.

"Of course there was a wave of sadness in Capernaum when the news came about the murder of James, but I cannot say that it was a surprise. The storm clouds on the horizon could be clearly seen, and no one expected that their path would be an easy one.

"And Sarah! One would think that the treatment she had received would cause her to be very careful about her involvement in the cause, but the opposite was true. A crowd gathered outside Zebedee's house, ostensively to share in his grief, but it turned into a time of rejoicing. There was great sympathy for Sarah when she told of her experience in Jerusalem, but her strength and joy were an inspiration to everyone. She told them, 'The day after our beatings as Alex and I were suffering together, an idea struck me like a flash of light. I cried out with such excitement that it startled Alex. "Alex," I cried, "that whipping post! That must be the same one they used when they beat our Lord! Not with rods, but with the terrible whip! We had the privilege to suffer for Him at the very spot where He suffered for us!" I cannot tell you what joy filled us at that thought. It turned our pain into blessing!' "

Then Castor said, "Livy, I tell you, such faith can conquer the world."

Livy put down his wax tablets and looked steadfastly at Castor and said, "You are a Christian, aren't you?"

"I am happy to say that I am," replied Castor, and Livy could not help but notice that his face reflected a joy that was most unusual. Then he said, "I'll tell you how it happened.

"A week after Alex and Sarah returned from Jerusalem, I retired from the army and left Capernaum for good. It was not easy saying good-bye to the folks I had lived with for years, and I knew when I left, I would never see them again. Yes, it was a sad parting for me. I went to Caesarea to board a ship for Rome, but, for some reason that I never learned, it was delayed. Since I had a few days to spend, I decided to stay with my centurion friend, Cornelius. The first evening with him, he told me an unbelievable story.

"Cornelius is an outstanding man, the kind of man that could be called a noble Roman, and sad to say, there are too few of them. He had given up on the Roman gods, just as I had, and in his heart, he was looking for a God to worship that was indeed worthy of a true heart's affection. You don't find many people with such desires! Now here's the unbelievable part; an angel of God appeared to him — I don't know whether this was a dream or not — but the angel told him to send for a man called Peter who would instruct him. But more than that — he gave him Peter's address!

"Peter! My friend from Capernaum! But I knew that Peter was a good Jew and would not have fellowship with a gentile. Although I was a friend of Peter, there was always a wall between us; he would never share a meal with me. You can imagine how surprised I was when Cornelius told me that Peter not only came into his house, but also told him that God had declared to him that the gentiles could enter the family of faith without becoming Jews. Could this be? Then he told me that he and many of his friends had been baptized and the presence of God had flooded into them. So here was a Roman centurion who was a baptized Christian. Of course, when I heard of this possibility, I was baptized the next day.

"Now let me finish my story. Agrippa was also in Caesarea for a great celebration in honor of Emperor Claudius. People from Tyre and Sidon were there in great numbers because they were about to enter into a peace treaty with Israel. They could see that King Agrippa's power was on the increase, and it was to their advantage to be on good terms with him. Cornelius and I decided to attend the celebration because we wanted to see this man who represented the greatest threat to the existence of Christians. I will admit that I harbored a personal anger against him because of what he had done to James and Alex and Sarah.

"It was a beautiful morning in Caesarea, bright and clear. The great amphitheater built by Herod the Great was filled to capacity, and we had trouble finding a seat. We were quite a distance from the dais, but this gave us ample opportunity to observe the reaction of the crowd. It was something I had never seen before, and I sincerely hope I will never see again. Agrippa was wearing a spectacular robe woven with threads of real silver. When he came out onto the dais, the slanting rays of the morning sun flashed against the silver strands creating an amazing display of light. As one person, the huge throng caught its breath in amazement. Then Agrippa slowly raised his arms to his sides, and the large triangular sleeves made him appear as a giant silver bird poised to take flight. It was indeed an amazing sight. Someone let out a shout, 'He is a god!' and soon the whole amphitheater resounded with the chant, 'He is a god! He is a god!'

"Agrippa did not call for silence; on the contrary, he turned slowly from side to side causing the reflections to change in a most unusual way. The shouting grew louder and more insistent, and everyone was overcome by religious frenzy.

"After a long, long time of enjoying the adulation, he began his oration. The crowd was in such a state that I am not sure they heard what he was saying. Then the shout went up, 'It is the voice of god, not of man!' And then the scene became unbelievable. Some began to raise their arms in worship; some cried out, 'O mighty god, forgive our sins; O god, have mercy on us!' Through it all, Agrippa stood with arms outstretched, accepting the praise, accepting the worship, clearly declaring that the crowd was right in assuming that he was a god.

"In the confusion, I turned to Cornelius and said to him, 'This is blasphemy! He is king of the Jews, but now he wants to be recognized as god. There is only one person who is entitled to be called King and God, and they crucified Him. Now Agrippa has set himself against His followers in an attempt to wipe out His name from history.' Then I prayed loud enough for Cornelius to hear, 'O Lord God of heaven and earth, behold the blasphemy of this man who takes to himself the honor that rightly belongs only to Your Holy Son. He has set himself against You and Your people. O Lord, do not allow this evil to go unavenged. Bare Your mighty arm, and bring judgment.'

"I did not even get a chance to say 'Amen.' Before our eyes, Agrippa ceased his oration, clutched his side and let out a loud, prolonged wail. The people around him rushed to steady him, but he fell to his knees in pain. In the confusion that followed, they picked him up, silver robe still flashing in the sun, and carried him out.

"For a long time, the people stood in stunned silence, and then a questioning murmur arose, getting louder and louder. What had happened? Had he been stabbed? Had someone poisoned him? After a considerable time, a deputy mounted the dais and called for quiet. Then he said, 'Our king has taken ill. He has severe pains in his stomach and we hope that this will pass soon. However, we cannot be sure how long it will take him to recover; consequently, the celebration is canceled.'

"A sigh of disappointment went up from the crowd, but no one in the place was as stunned as I was. Had we witnessed the judgment of God before our very eyes? Did this judgment have anything to do with the murder of James and Agrippa's determination to wipe out the Christians? We were filled with questions, but no answers.

" 'Perhaps he will be better by tomorrow,' Cornelius said to me. 'If he is, that will answer some of our questions.' I agreed with him. But he did not recover the next day, nor the next. He suffered for five days, and then he died!

"Now you know the rest of the story. Rome determined that there would no longer be a king in Israel and the land was annexed to Syria. The reign of the Herods was over! There would be no more kings for the Jews."

"And what will happen to Israel now?" asked Livy.

"I do not know," replied Castor, "but the future does not look good. They have no leader of their own now, and they will not accept the domination of Rome. It will come to a showdown, and Israel cannot possibly win."

"And the Christians?" asked Livy.

"For the Christians I see increasing persecution, perhaps even here in Rome, perhaps even for me; but the flame will never be extinguished. It will burn forever!"

Dear Reader:

Please let us know how you feel about Barbour Books' Christian Fiction.

1. What most influenced you to purchase **Biblical Novel Collection** #1, #2, #3, #4, #5, (Please circle one)?

   ____ Author   ____ Recommendations

   ____ Subject matter   ____ Price

   ____ Cover / titles

2. Would you buy other books in the **Biblical Novel Collection** series by this author?

   ____ Yes   ____ No

3. Where did you purchase this book?

   ____ Christian book store   ____ Other

   ____ General book store   ____ Mail order

4. What is your overall rating of this **Biblical Novel Collection**?

   ____ Excellent ____ Very good ____ Good ____ Fair ____ Poor

5. How many hours a week do you spend reading books? ____ hrs.

6. Are you a member of a church? ____ Yes ____ No

   If yes, what denomination?_____

7. Please check age

   ____ Under 18   ____ 25-34   ____ 45-54

   ____ 18-24   ____ 35-44   ____ 55 and over

Mail to: **Fiction Editor**
Barbour Books
P.O. Box 719
Uhrichsville, OH 44683

NAME _____

ADDRESS _____

CITY _____ STATE _____ ZIP _____

Thank you for helping us provide the best in Christian fiction!